Fishes of the Red Sea

ALBERTO SILIOTTI

GEODIA EDIZIONI

Text Alberto Siliotti
Technical profiles (bony fishes) Martina Milanese
Photographs Manfred Bortoli
Drawings Stefania Cossu

Project Editor Yvonne Marzo
Editor Elisa Marti
Scientific advise Angelo Mojet
English translation Richard Pierc

Printed in Egypt

Distributed in Egypt by GeoEgypt (Sharm el-Sheikh

ISBN 99-97177-42-2

How to Use This Guide

The Red Sea and Its Fauna

The Coral Reef

Cartilaginous Fishes
Sharks 17 • Rays 33

Bony Fishes
Morays – Eels 49 • Lizardfishes – Frogfishes 57 •
Soldierfishes – Squirrelfishes 63 • Cornetfishes –
Needlefishes 69 • Lionfishes – Stonefishes –
Crocodilefishes 75 • Groupers – Anthias 85 •
Bigeyes – Cardinalfishes 103 • Grunts – Breams 109
• Batfishes 115 • Snappers 119 • Fusiliers 127 •
Emperorfishes 133 • Sweepers – Glassfishes 139 •
Goatfishes 145 • Angelfishes 153 • Butterflyfishes
161 • Hawkfishes 177 • Damselfishes – Pullers –
Anemonefishes – Sargeantfishes 183 •
Cleanerfishes – Napoleonfishes – Wrasses – 203 •
Parrotfishes 215 • Barracuda 225 • Blennies –
Gobies 229 • Surgeonfishes – Unicornfishes –
Rabbitfishes 235 • Trevallies 253 • Triggerfishes –
Filefishes 263 • Boxfishes – Pufferfishes –
Porcupinefishes 277

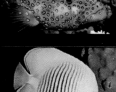

Bibliography

Index

ommon
name

Scientific
name

Name of author
and year
species was
first described

Maximum si
and habitat
species

1

Whitetip Reef Shark

Triaenodon obesus (Ruppel, 1827)

I	Squalo a pinna bianca di scogliera
D	Weißspitzenriffhai
F	Requin à ailerons blancs

213 cm

1-40 m

CARCHARHINIFORMES

Carcharhinidae

Description

The adults can be as long as 2.13 meters. The tips of the two dor
fins and the caudal fin are white. Dorsally its body is greyish-brow
while ventrally it is light grey or silver.

Habitat

This shark usually dwells along the outer slopes of the coral re
from 40 meters depth to the surface.

Sometimes during the day it can be spotted resting in caves or
the sandy sea bottom.

Distribution

Red Sea and Indo-Pacific region.

Biology and Behavior

A "creature of habit," this reef shark feeds mostly on fish and cre
taceans, generally at night. The females give birth to 1-5 young, wh
are 50 centimeters long on an average.

When and how to observe species (night / day, scuba or snorkelling)

Typical features of species

Common name

Scientific name

Index of dangerousness

Cartilaginous fishes

Bony fishes

Dangerous (if approached or if touched)

Body profile of family or genus

Illustration of species described

Special or curious features

Page number

Reef zones of distribution

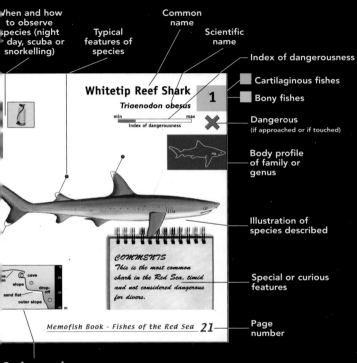

Whitetip Reef Shark 1

Triaenodon obesus

min |————————————| max
index of dangerousness

COMMENTS
This is the most common shark in the Red Sea, timid and not considered dangerous for divers.

Memofish Book - Fishes of the Red Sea **21**

cave
slope
drop-off
sand flat
outer slope

5

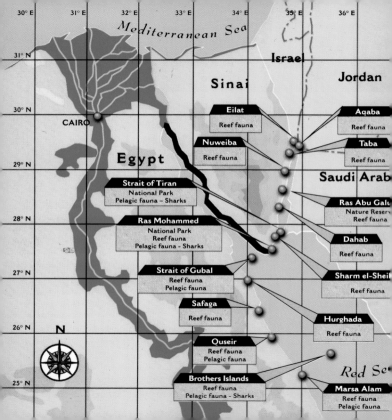

THE RED SEA AND ITS FAUNA

The Red Sea is a narrow body of water 2,250 kilometers long and with an average width of 300 kilometers that lies between Asia and Africa. Its formation began about 40,000,000 years ago when these two continental plates separated and the Arabian peninsula rose up. This tectonic movement is still continuing and the plates are moving apart at the incredible rate of 2.5 centimeters per year. Consequently, in 100,000,000 years this sea will be 2,500 kilometers wide, which is why geologists have called it "an ocean in the making." The Red Sea, which has a maximum depth of 2,860 meters, is connected to the Indian Ocean only by the narrow southern Strait of Bab el-Mandeb. Its water is therefore salty and warm; the average salinity is 42%, as opposed to 38% in the Indian Ocean, while the average temperature of the Gulf of Aqaba in the month of February is high, 20 °C.

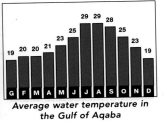

Average water temperature in the Gulf of Aqaba

The Red Sea is known for its extraordinary coral reef and abundance of fauna, which includes over one thousand species of fishes, 10% of which are endemic (that is, they are to be found only in this body of water). Among these endemic species, seven are butterflyfishes belonging to the Chaetodontidae family.

Distribution of fauna in the Indo-Pacific region

Indian Ocean endemic species 13%
Red Sea endemic species 17%
Indo-Pacific tropical species 70%

As a habitat, the Red Sea has two major groups of fishes, reef and pelagic.

Reef fishes, as their name implies, live around the coral reef and are generally small or medium-sized. They have bright colors and their feeding habits are extremely varied: some live on plankton, others are herbivorous, and yet others are either carnivorous or omnivorous. There are about 300 species of reef fishes, some of which live alone, others in couples and in large schools. Then there are certain species that are often associated with particular soft or stony corals.

Pelagic fishes, on the other hand, prefer to roam in the open; these are mostly carnivorous species that approach the outer edge of the coral reef, which is rich in fauna, to find their food.

Both reef fishes and pelagic fishes include species with basically diurnal o

A group of butterflyfish in the Sharm el-Sheikh reef

nocturnal habits, that is, they are active during the day or night. Given the abundance of fauna in the Red Sea, the great interest in its complex ecosystem, and the boom in tourism that has given rise to the many tourist facilities along the coastline, in 1983 the Egyptian government instituted the first nature reserve in Sinai, the *Ras Mohammed National Park*, which later grew in size by incorporating other areas (the Strait of Tiran, Nabq, Ras Abu Galum and Taba).

In all these areas tourists must observe the park regulations in order to safeguard the environment.

PARK REGULATIONS

 Do not touch or break any corals or shells.

  Fishing and spearfishing are not allowed in Protected Areas.

 Do not collect or damage any material, either living or dead (corals, shells, fish, plants, fossils, etc.).

 It is prohibited to throw refuse of any kind into the sea.

 It is prohibited to access any closed area and to walk or anchor on any reef area. Please use marked access points.

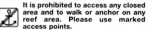

 Access to diving areas is recommended at designated access points only. This reduces damage to reef areas.

 Fish feeding is prohibited as it upsets the biological balance of the reef.

 Offenders are subject to prosecution according to the terms of Law 102 of 1983.

THE CORAL REEF

Extending for over 2,000 kilometers along the coasts of the Red Sea is an extraordinarily long coral reef, consisting of colonies of tiny organisms known as **polyps**.

From a morphological standpoint, almost all the Red Sea coral reefs are **fringing reefs**, which are characterized by "young" reefs about 5,000-7,000 years old that grow only a few meters away from the coastline; they are shaped like fringes and grow outwardly.

Fringing reefs have various components, each of which is distinguished by specific fauna: **a.** the **coralline platform** covered with 30-80 centimeters of water is just off the coastline and may sometimes turn into a true **lagoon**; **b. the slope**, which descends for 10-30 meters and often has grottoes; this is made up of **stony corals** belonging for the most part to the *Acropora*

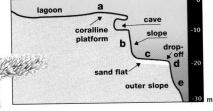

The structure of a fringing reef

Porites *sp.*

Acropora *sp.*

and *Porites* genera; **c.** the **sand flat**; **d.** the **drop-off**, the point between the sand flat and the outer slope; **e.** the **outer slope**, or outer edge of the reef, which may descend for hundreds of meters into the sea. Not all the above elements are always present: for example, the lagoon may be missing or may be very large; the same is true of the sand flat. However, in all fringing reefs, the families

Alcyonacean

of corals that form their structure have a particular distribution depending on the depth, temperature, currents and wave motion. Besides the stony corals, fringing reefs have other corals, known as soft corals or **Alcyonacea**, which have no hard calcareous exoskeleton and follow the movement of the waves, and **Gorgonians**, which form large fans on the outer slopes of the reef, at a depth of 12-38 meters.

WARNING
While exploring the reef and observing its marvelous fauna, make sure not to touch the so-called fire coral (*Millepora dichotoma*): the tentacles of its polyps sting and may cause painful burns.

Gorgonian

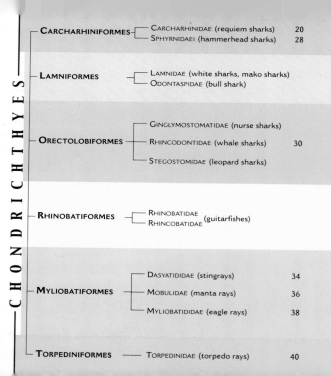

CHONDRICHTHYES

CARCHARHINIFORMES
- CARCHARHINIDAE (requiem sharks) — 20
- SPHYRNIDAEI (hammerhead sharks) — 28

LAMNIFORMES
- LAMNIDAE (white sharks, mako sharks)
- ODONTASPIDAE (bull shark)

ORECTOLOBIFORMES
- GINGLYMOSTOMATIDAE (nurse sharks)
- RHINCODONTIDAE (whale sharks) — 30
- STEGOSTOMIDAE (leopard sharks)

RHINOBATIFORMES
- RHINOBATIDAE (guitarfishes)
- RHINCOBATIDAE

MYLIOBATIFORMES
- DASYATIDIDAE (stingrays) — 34
- MOBULIDAE (manta rays) — 36
- MYLIOBATIDIDAE (eagle rays) — 38

TORPEDINIFORMES
- TORPEDINIDAE (torpedo rays) — 40

CARTILAGINOUS FISHES

From an anatomical standpoint, fish are grouped into two large classes: **Chondrichthyes**, or **cartilaginous fishes** (with a cartilaginous skeleton), which includes sharks and rays; and **Osteichthyes** which comprises all the other fish that have a bone skeleton. There are more than 1100 species of Chondrichthyes, and in the Red Sea they are represented by both sharks and rays.

Both these are characterized by their teeth being continually replaced during their lifetime and by reproduction through internal fecundation, which occurs by means of the male sexual organs, called *pterigopods*, which inject sperm into the female's genital apparatus.

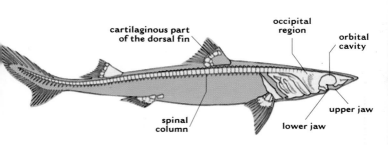

The skeletal structure of a typical cartilaginous fish (shark)

Carcharhinus amblyrhynchos (#2)

SHARKS

Sharks are ancient fishes that have been living in all the world's seas for about 430,000,000 years. They are grouped into six orders with about 500 species, 44 of which live in the Red Sea. Among these latter, about ten, most of which belong to the **Carcharhinidae** family, can also be seen in the northern Red Sea. The two most common species are the *whitetip reef shark* and the *blacktip reef shark*, the average size of which is 150-200 centimeters. The identification of sharks is based on an observation of

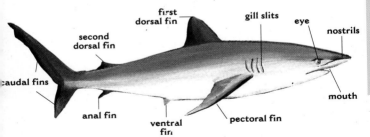

Morphology of a shark

Common genera in the Red Sea:
Triaenodon, Carcharhinus, Nebrius, Rhincodon, Sphyrna.

17

their fins and body. Three categories can be distinguished: sharks with special marking on their fins; sharks with special marking on their body; sharks without any particular marking. Most sharks have a limited perception of color but seem able to spot profiles against the light and are attracted by shiny objects. Their sense of smell is extremely keen, as is manifested by the exceptional development of the cerebral regions used for this sense, which may consist of as much as 60% of the entire cephalic mass. Sharks also have extraordinary hearing and above all they have an incredible capacity to perceive variations of one tenmillionenth of a volt in an electric field, which means they can detect the presence of possible prey without even seeing it thanks to special receptor organs known as the "ampullae of Lorenzini" in the head region. In general, sharks are rather slow swimmers, moving at an average speed of 5-10 km per hour, but in the case of an

SHARK ATTACKS AGAINST HUMANS

Total attacks per year	50
Australia	6
Brazil	5
South Africa	4
Florida	5
California + Hawaii	6
Red Sea	0
Other areas	24

attack they are capable of sudden bursts of speed and can attain a velocity of 60-100 kilometers per hour in a few seconds. Many genera of sharks have weak branchiomeric musculature and are forced to move about constantly in order to increase the circulation of water in their respiratory system, which in turn augments the flow of oxygen in their blood. The shape of sharks' teeth varies according to the species and feeding habits. They are arranged in two parallel rows; only the outer teeth are used, while the inner ones, which are slowly moved forward, serve to replace the former when they are broken or deteriorated. Although sharks' behavior is generally unpredictable, the ones that live in the northern Red Sea are not considered dangerous for humans, and in recent years they have not attacked divers or swimmers. However, it is best to be cautious; they should be observed from a safe distance and their territory should not be invaded.

Carcharhinus amblyrhynchos (#2)

CARCHARHINIFORMES

Carcharhinidae

Whitetip Reef Shark

Triaenodon obesus (Ruppel, 1827)

I **Squalo a pinna bianca di scogliera**
D **Weißspitzenriffhai**
F **Requin à ailerons blancs**

213 cm

1-40 m

Description
The adults can be as long as 2.13 meters. The tips of the two dorsal fins and the caudal fin are white. Dorsally its body is greyish-brown, while ventrally it is light grey or silver.

Habitat
This shark usually dwells along the outer slopes of the coral reef, from 40 meters depth to the surface.
Sometimes during the day it can be spotted resting in caves or on the sandy sea bottom.

Distribution
Red Sea and Indo-Pacific region.

Biology and Behavior
A "creature of habit," this reef shark feeds mostly on fish and crustaceans, generally at night. The females give birth to 1-5 young, which are 50 centimeters long on an average.

Whitetip Reef Shark

Triaenodon obesus

min ▬▬▬▬▬▬ max
index of dangerousness

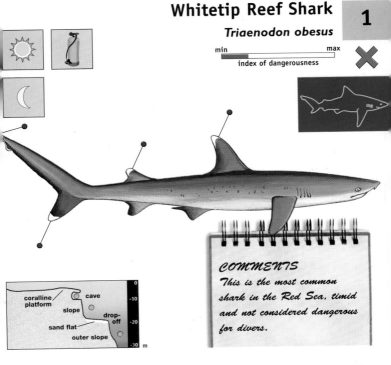

COMMENTS
This is the most common shark in the Red Sea, timid and not considered dangerous for divers.

coralline platform · cave · slope · drop-off · sand flat · outer slope

0 · -10 · -20 · -30 m

Grey Reef Shark

Carcharhinus amblyrhynchos (Bleeker. 1856)

I **Squalo grigio di scogliera**
D **Grauer Riffhai**
F **Requin gris de récif**

255 cm

0-280 m

Description

A shark with a massive body that can be as long as 2.55 meters.
It is grey dorsally and white ventrally. The second dorsal fin, the ventral fins and the anal fin are black; the caudal margin has a wide blackish band.

Habitat

The grey reef shark lives along the outer slopes of the coral reef, from the surface to 280 meters' depth, and in lagoons near zones with strong currents.

Distribution

Red Sea and Indo-Pacific region.

Biology and Behavior

This shark has a curious character. It feeds mainly on small fish but also likes crustaceans. Sexual maturity is reached at the age of seven and the maximum longevity is 25 years. The females give birth to 1-6 young that are 40-60 centimeters long on an average.

Grey Reef Shark

Carcharhinus amblyrhynchos

min   max

index of dangerousness

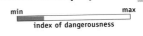

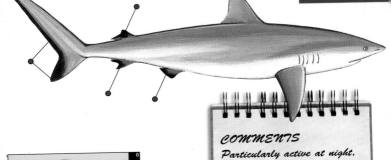

COMMENTS
Particularly active at night,
tends to be aggressive in the
presence of food. Potentially
dangerous for humans.

coralline platform
cave
slope
drop-off
sand flat
outer slope

0
-10
-20
-30 m

Silvertip Shark

Carcharhinus albimarginatus (Ruppel, 1827)

- **I** **Squalo dalle punte argentee**
- **D** **Silberspitzenhai**
- **F** **Requin à pointes blanches**

300 cm

0-800 m

CARCHARHINIFORMES

Carcharhinidae

Description

A powerful shark that may weigh up to 160 kilograms.
It is dorsally dark grey or brownish-grey and ventrally white. The dorsal and pectoral fins are whitish, as are the tips of the caudal fin lobes and the caudal margin.

Habitat

It generally frequents the open sea but also roams in coastal waters, where it may be seen along the outer slope of the coral reef.

Distribution

Red Sea, Indo-Pacific region and Atlantic Ocean.

Biology and Behavior

It feeds mainly on fish and sometimes on cephalopods, rays and even other smaller sharks. The female gives birth to up to 11 young.

Silvertip Shark

3

Carcharhinus albimarginatus

min   max
index of dangerousness

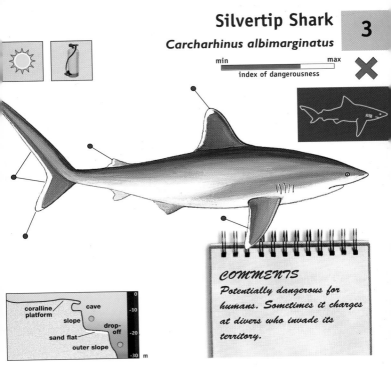

COMMENTS
Potentially dangerous for
humans. Sometimes it charges
at divers who invade its
territory.

coralline platform
cave
slope
drop-off
sand flat
outer slope

0
-10
-20
-30 m

CARCHARHINIFORMES

Carcharhinidae

Blacktip Reef Shark

Carcharhinus melanopterus (Quoy & Gaymard,1824)

I **Squalo pinne nere di scogliera**
D **Schwarzspitzen-Riffhai**
F **Requin à pointes noires**

180 cm

20-75 m

Description

A small shark whose body is yellow-brownish dorsally and white v[e]ntrally. It is easy to identify because the upper part of the first dorsal (which is quite prominent) and the lower lobe of the caudal fin [are] blackish apically, preceded by a white stripe.

Habitat

It is commonly seen in shallow water near reefs, on the reef platfor[m] in lagoons and on sandy bottoms.

Distribution

Red Sea, Indo-Pacific region, eastern Mediterranean.

Biology and Behavior

This shark likes the reef, in shallow water or near the drop-offs, feedi[ng] on fish as well as crustaceans and mollusks. It often rests during the d[ay] in caves or reef shelters. Although it is timid, it can become aggressi[ve] if it feels it is in danger.

Blacktip Reef Shark

4

Carcharhinus melanopterus

min ▬▬▬▬ max
index of dangerousness

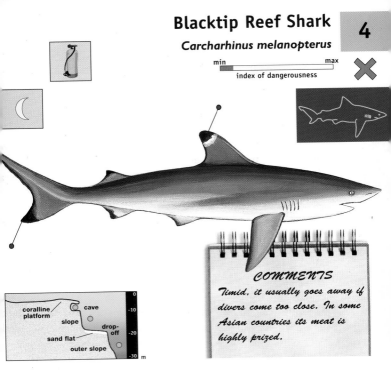

COMMENTS
Timid, it usually goes away if divers come too close. In some Asian countries its meat is highly prized.

coralline platform
cave
slope
drop-off
sand flat
outer slope
0
-10
-20
-30 m

Scalloped Hammerhead Shark

5

Sphyrna lewini (Griffith&Smith, 1834)

I **Squalo martello smerlato**
D **Gekerbter Hammerhai**
F **Petit requin-marteau**

430 cm

0-275 m

CARCHARHINIFORMES

Sphyrnidae

Description
A shark of medium to large size (it may weigh over 150 kilograms) that is easily recognizable for its long, flat head perpendicular to the body, with the eyes on the sides.
The body is grey, sometimes with brownish or olive-green hues without any particular marking.

Habitat
A pelagic and coastal shark, it often approaches the outer slope of reefs. Some schools live here permanently, while others migrate.

Distribution
All tropical seas and temperate-warm waters.

Biology and Behavior
It feeds mainly on fish, but also likes cephalopods, crustaceans and rays. The young sharks often live in schools that may number over 100 members; the adults are solitary or live in couples. The females give birth to 15-30 young that are 40-50 centimeters long.

Scalloped Hammerhead Shark

5

Sphyrna lewini

min ▬▬▬▬▬▬ max
index of dangerousness

COMMENTS

*In many countries it is killed
mercilessly for its meat.
Potentially dangerous, but not
often aggressive with divers.*

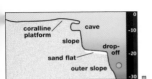

coralline platform — cave — slope — drop-off — sand flat — outer slope
0, -10, -20, -30 m

Whale Shark

Rhincodon typus (Smith, 1828)

I **Squalo balena**
D **Walhai**
F **Requin-baleine**

 1300 cm

 0-140 m

ORECTOLOBIFORMES

Rhincodontidae

Description

The whale shark is the largest fish in the world; it can be up to 13 meters long and it weighs 20 tons. Its bluish-grey body is dotted with white spots and lined with white bands. The gigantic caudal fin is crescent-shaped. Its enormous mouth is at the end of its body, not recessed, and has extremely small teeth. Five huge branchial slits lie on each side.

Habitat

A pelagic shark that often skirts the reef, going into bays and other protected areas.

Distribution

Red Sea and all tropical and sub-tropical seas.

Biologia e comportamento

It swims slowly near the surface in search of plankton, small fish and crustaceans.

It is solitary, or lives in couples or schools, and is migratory.

Whale Shark

Rhincodon typus

6

min ▬▬▬▬▬▬ max
index of dangerousness

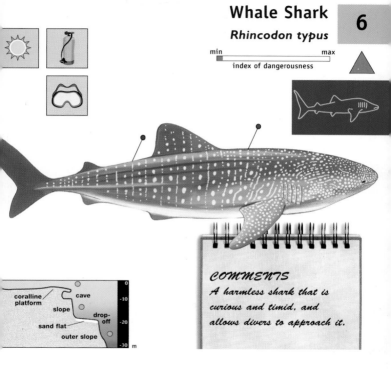

COMMENTS
A harmless shark that is curious and timid, and allows divers to approach it.

coralline platform
cave
slope
drop-off
sand flat
outer slope
0
-10
-20
-30 m

Taeniura lymma (#7)

RAYS

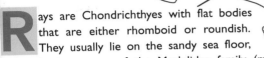

Rays are Chondrichthyes with flat bodies that are either rhomboid or roundish. They usually lie on the sandy sea floor, although the genera of the Modulidae family (manta rays) and Miliobatidae (eagle rays) prefer the surface of the open sea. While resting on the bottom, rays take in water through two orifices called *spiracles* situated at either side of the eyes. Their gill slits and mouth are on the ventral side.

spiracle

eyes

ventral fins

DORSAL VIEW

spiracle

venomous spines

anus

gill slits

The morphology of rays

ventral fins

nostrils **VENTRAL VIEW**

mouth

Common genera in the Red Sea:
Taeniura, Manta, Aetobatus, Torpedo.

33

Dasyatidae

Mobulidae

Myliobatididae

Torpedinidae

Blue-Spotted Stingray

Taeniura lymma (Forsskål, 1775)

I **Trigone a macchie blu**
D **Blaupunktrochen**
F **Pastenague à taches bleues**

70 cm

1-20 m

Description

An extremely common species in the Red Sea that is often 70 cm long. It is distinguished by its disk-shaped body, which is yellowish with many round blue spots on the dorsal side and white ventrally. Its long tail has two serrated venomous spines.

Habitat

It prefers sandy, shallow bottoms near reefs, caves and other sheltered spots where it rests half buried in the sand.

Distribution

Red Sea and Indo-Pacific region up to Australia and Japan.

Biology and Behavior

This stingray feeds on mollusks, shrimp and worms and is very timid. It looks for food during high tide or at night. It is ovovivparous: the eggs develop and hatch inside the mother's body.

Blue-Spotted Stingray

Taeniura lymma

min   max
index of dangerousness

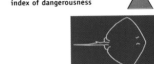

venomous
spines

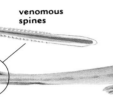

COMMENTS

Its sting is painful but not lethal. Fished widely for its meat and as an aquarium species.

coralline platform   cave
slope
sand flat   drop-off
outer slope

Manta Ray

Manta birostris (Walbaum, 1792)

I **Manta gigante**
D **Mantarochen**
F **Raie manta**

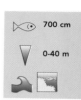

700 cm

0-40 m

Description

The manta ray's body has two enormous "wings" and two large cephalic horn-like fins that it uses to change direction and to push plankton into its mouth. This latter is situated at the end of the body, between the ventral and dorsal sides. There are no spines on its tail.

Habitat

Manta rays prefer shallow water near reefs or sheltered bays. It has been seen in the open sea.

Distribution

Red Sea, Atlantic Ocean, Indo-Pacific region.

Biology and Behavior

Despite its huge size, this species is inoffensive and not aggressive. It feeds mainly on plankton but sometimes eats small fish and crustaceans. Manta rays are ovoviviparous; during the mating season they gather in small schools.

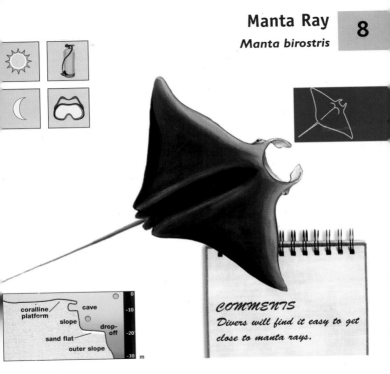

coralline platform
cave
slope
drop-off
sand flat
outer slope

0
-10
-20
-30 m

COMMENTS
Divers will find it easy to get close to manta rays.

Spotted Eagle Ray

Aetobatus narinari (Euphrasen, 1790)

I **Aquila di mare maculata**
D **Adlerrochen**
F **Raie léopard**

230 cm

1-45 m

MYLIOBATIFORMES

Myliobatididae

Description
Dorsally, the spotted eagle ray is dark grey or bluish grey with many small white spots, while its ventral side is white. Its mouth has robust flat teeth that allow it to break shells and its tail has serrate venomous spines at the base.

Habitat
The spotted eagle ray likes shallow water in bays and lagoons near reefs, but also travels for long distances in the open sea. It swims on the surface and sometimes rests on the sandy bottoms.

Distribution
Red Sea, Indo-Pacific region and western Atlantic Ocean.

Biology and Behavior
It feeds on mollusks, crustaceans, and sometimes octopus and small fish. It sometimes lives in schools or in couples, especially during the mating season. It is ovoviviparous and gestation lasts about one year.

Spotted Eagle Ray

Aetobatus narinari

min ———————— max
index of dangerousness

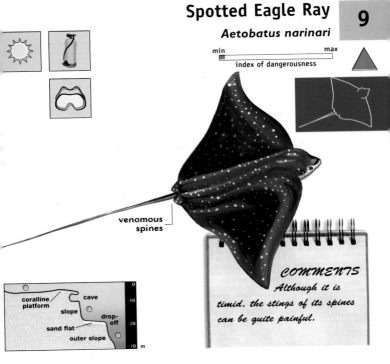

venomous
spines

COMMENTS
Although it is timid, the stings of its spines can be quite painful.

coralline platform
cave
slope
drop-off
sand flat
outer slope
0
-10
-20
-30 m

Panther Torpedo Ray

Torpedo panthera Olphers, 1831

- I **Torpedine pantera**
- D **Bogenstirn Torpedorochen**
- F **Torpille panthère**

100 cm

0-110 m

Description

The disk-shaped body ends in a long, robust, spineless tail.
Its dorsal side has a great many yellow-brownish patches, and the
two dorsal fins and two pectoral fins lie near the caudal fin. Its ventral side is whitish.

Habitat

The panther torpedo ray lives on sandy sea floors or near reef
slopes, generally in shallow water.

Distribution

Red Sea, western Indian Ocean.

Biology and Behavior

This ray feeds on crustaceans, worms and tiny fish, which it captures
by using special organs on the sides of its body consisting of
muscular tissue that generate electric current of 100-200 volts.

Panther Torpedo Ray

Torpedo panthera

10

min ▭ max
index of dangerousness

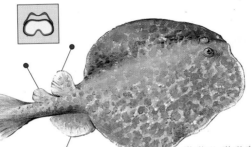

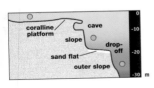

coralline platform
cave
slope
drop-off
sand flat
outer slope

0
-10
-20
-30 m

COMMENTS
The electric shocks generated by this ray are not dangerous for humans but may cause temporary unconsciousness.

OSTEICHTHYES

ANGUILLIFORMES
- MURAENIDAE (morays) — 49
- CONGRIDAE (conger eels)
- HETEROCONGRIDAE (garden eels) — 49

AULOPIFORMES
- SYNODONTIDAE (lizardfishes) — 57

LOPHIFORMES
- ANTENNARIIDAE (anglerfishes) — 57

BERYCIFORMES
- HOLOCENTRIDAE (soldierfishes, squirrelfishes) — 63

SYNGNATHIFORMES
- FISTULARIIDAE (trumpetfishes) — 69

BELONIFORMES
- BELONIDAE (needlefishes) — 69

SCORPAENIFORMES
- SCORPAENIDAE (lionfishes, stonefishes) — 75
- PLATYCEPHALIDAE (crocodilefishes) — 75

PERCIFORMES
- SERRANIDAE (groupers, anthias) — 85
- PRIACANTHIDAE (bigeyes) — 103
- APOGONIDAE (cardinalfishes) — 103
- HAEMULIDAE (grunts, breams) — 109
- EPHIPPIDAE (batfishes) — 115
- LUTJANIDAE (dentexes, snappers) — 119
- CAESIONIDAE (fusiliers) — 127
- LETHRINIDAE (emperorfishes) — 133
- PEMPHERIDAE (sweepers, glassfishes) — 139
- MULLIDAE (goatfishes) — 145
- POMACANTHIDAE (angelfishes) — 153
- CHAETODONTIDAE (butterflyfishes) — 161
- CIRRHITIDAE (hawkfishes) — 177
- POMACENTRIDAE (damselfishes, chromis, anemonefishes, sergeantfishe
- LABRIDAE (cleaners, napoleonfishes, wrasses) — 203
- SCARIDAE (parrotfishes) — 215
- SPHYRAENIDAE (barracuda) — 225
- BLENNIDAE (blennies) — 229
- GOBIIDAE (gobies) — 229
- ACANTHURIDAE (surgeonfishes, unicornfishes) — 235
- SIGANIDAE (rabbitfishes) — 235
- CARANGIDAE (trevallies) — 253

TETRAODONTIFORMES
- BALISTIDAE (triggerfishes) — 263
- MONACANTHIDAE (filefishes) — 263
- OSTRACIIDAE (boxfishes) — 277
- TETRAODONTIDAE (pufferfishes) — 277
- DIODONTIDAE (porcupinefishes) — 277

NOTE

This chart has been simplified and adapted to the families described in this volume.

BONY FISHES

Bony fishes, or **Osteichthyes**, are distinguished by their skeletal structures, which consist of bony tissue and differ from the cartilaginous tissue of the Chondrichthyes.
There are many more families and species (over 25,000) of bony than cartilaginous fishes. Their habitat is also much larger, since their distribution ranges from the sea surface to the ocean abysses, where some species live at a depth of more than 10,000 meters. There are great morphological differences among the Osteichthyes, but they also have many basic features in common: a system of fins consisting of paired fins (pec-

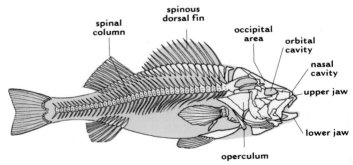

Skeletal structure of a typical bony fish

toral and ventral or pelvic) and unpaired fins (dorsal, anal and caudal or tail). In general it is the tail fin that has different shapes and that is used for propulsion, while the other fins are stabilizers. However, in some families the dorsal or pectoral fins are used to propel the fish.

The fins of most Osteichthyes have **horny rays** that may be either hard or soft and are basic elements in the identification and classification of these species. The **cranium** of bony fishes is made up of connected osseous plates and in 95% of the species the body is covered with **scales** that rest on an epithelial tissue rich in chromatophores or **pigment-bearing cells**. With these cells the fish can change pigmentation or assume particular patterns in relation to its species, sex, age, habitat, and even its "mood." Unlike cartilaginous fishes, most bony fishes have an eversion of the intestine known as the **swim bladder** that allows them to maintain a horizontal position and to move at various depths.

All these fishes have a special sensory organ, the **lateral line**, made up of a series of orifices on its sides between the cranium and the tail; this allows them to perceive, at a distance, variations in hydrostatic pressure caused by their own movement, by the presence of other fish or by currents and, hence, to control their direction with great precision.

Lastly, all bony fishes have **gills** that are not exposed, as is the case with cartilaginous fishes, but are covered with **operculi**.

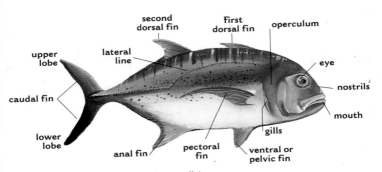

Morphology of a typical bony fish (trevally)

Gills play a basic role in breathing and their special structure allows the fish to absorb 74% of the oxygen in sea water. As for reproduction, all bony fishes are oviparous: the females either lay their eggs in a spot chosen and made suitable by the male, or deposit them in the water, where the male fertilizes them. The number of eggs, which in reef fishes have an average diameter of about one millimeter, varies quite a lot (the females of some genera lay more than one million), and it takes about one week for the formation of the larvae, which are adapted to life in pelagic waters. The period between the larval stage and the juvenile stage of the fish also varies greatly, from a few days to two months.

HOW TO IDENTIFY A FISH

CLASSIFICATION SYSTEM (simplified)

Example: *Caranx sexfasciatus*

Class	**Osteichthyes**
Order	Perciformes
Family	Carangidae
Genus	*Caranx*
Species	*sexfasciatus*

fusiform   com

SPOTS OR PATTERNS ON THE BODY

presen
of spe

presen
of so
or spino
ra

At present, there are over 25,000 known species of fish, and this number increases every year. The scientific classification of fish, created in 1758 by the Swedish naturalist Carl von Linnaeus, is based on a Latin name for every genus and species that often reflects their appearance (shape, color, size, number and position of fins, etc.).

heterocercal (the upper lobe is more developed than the lower one)

diphyocercal (only one rounded lobe) — **CAUDAL FIN**

homocercal (the upper and lower lobes are symmetrical with respect to the body)

LATERAL LINE

rounded

truncate

forked

SCALES —

absen

preser

crescent-shaped

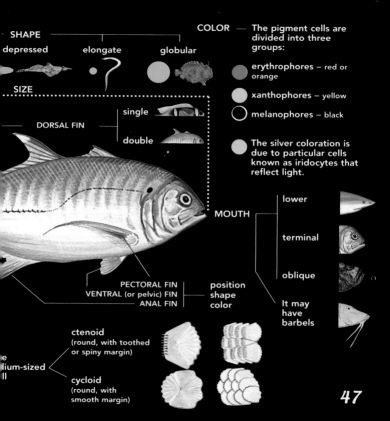

SHAPE

depressed   elongate   globular

SIZE

COLOR — The pigment cells are divided into three groups:

erythrophores — red or orange

xanthophores — yellow

melanophores — black

The silver coloration is due to particular cells known as iridocytes that reflect light.

DORSAL FIN
single
double

PECTORAL FIN
VENTRAL (or pelvic) FIN
ANAL FIN

position
shape
color

MOUTH
lower
terminal
oblique
It may have barbels

ctenoid
(round, with toothed or spiny margin)

cycloid
(round, with smooth margin)

e
lium-sized
ll

47

Gymnothorax javanicus (#11)

MORAYS AND EELS

Morays belong to the family of **Muraenidae**, which are characterized by a long, lithe, scaleless body; their length ranges from 20 to over 300 centimeters, so that they look like sea serpents. Moray eels have two round branchial clefts without operculi, their dorsal and anal fins are joined to the caudal fin, and they have no pectoral fins. There are 13 genera and about 200 species of morays. Morays are predatory fish with a highly developed sense of smell that feed on fish and crustaceans. During the day they usually linger in the fissures of reefs, with only their heads sticking out, and come out to feed when it gets dark. Morays almost always have their mouths open, not as a form of intimidation but in order to facilitate blood oxygenation by chanelling more water into their gills.

They have powerful, fearsome teeth that can crush the hardest crustacean shells, but in the main are timid creatures. However, it is best not to touch them, as they might react with very painful bites and the wounds inflicted are easily subject to secondary infections. Although morays are fished for their tender and tasty meat, bear in mind that some species can be highly toxic.

Common genera in the Red Sea:
Gymnothorax, Siderea, Gorgasia, Gymnomuraena, Echidna.

Giant Moray

Gymnothorax javanicus (Bleeker, 1859)

I	**Murena gigante**
D	**Riesenmuräne**
F	**Murène géante**

 300 cm

2-50 m

ANGUILLIFORMES

Muraenidae

Description

This moray has a massive body that can be as long as three meters and weigh up to 30 kilograms. The body is brown with darker, leopard-like spots in the adults, and two black blotches mark the branchial clefts. Its teeth are long and sharp.

Habitat

Typical of reef slopes up to 50 meters' depth, it lives in coral crevices, but sometimes emerges for brief periods.

Distribution

Red Sea and Indo-Pacific region.

Biology and Behavior

A nocturnal predator, it feeds mostly on fish and, less often, on crustaceans. It lives in symbiosis with cleaner shrimp that eliminate residue food or parasites, even inside the moray's mouth. The juveniles take refuge in shallow lagoon waters.

Giant Moray

 11

Gymnothorax javanicus

min   max
index of dangerousness

COMMENTS

The largest moray eel in the Indo-Pacific region. Though usually timid, if provoked it can deal painful bites.

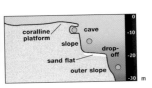

coralline platform · cave
slope
drop-off
sand flat
outer slope

0
-10
-20
-30 m

Grey Moray

Siderea grisea (Lacepède, 1803)

I **Murena grigia**
D **Graue Muräne**
F **Murène tatouée**

65 cm

1-40 m

Description

A medium-sized moray, 65 centimeters long. The body is slightly compressed, pale grey with yellowish blotches. The head is darker and has evident lines made up of small black spots.

Habitat

The grey moray is found in coastal waters, both in lagoons and along reef slopes up to 40 meters' depth.

Distribution

Indian Ocean, more frequent in the Red Sea.

Biology and Behavior

The juveniles often congregate in small groups in lairs among the corals. A typical nocturnal predator.

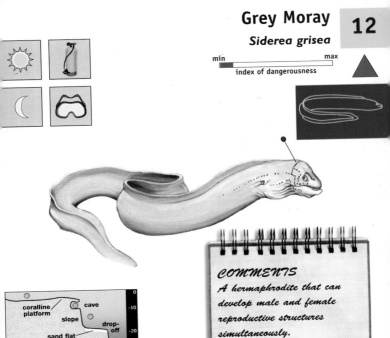

Grey Moray

Siderea grisea

12

min ————————— max
index of dangerousness

coralline platform
cave
slope
sand flat
drop-off
outer slope

0
-10
-20
-30 m

COMMENTS
A hermaphrodite that can develop male and female reproductive structures simultaneously.

Red Sea Garden Eel

Gorgasia sillneri (Klausewitz, 1962)

I **Eterocongride di Sillner**
D **Rotmeer-Röhrenaal**
F **Anguille jardinière de Mer Rouge**

83 cm

5-100 m

Description

Elongate body, with a rounded and tapering end. The skin has no scales and is pale grey. The short, slightly pointed head has opalescent spots. It may be as much as 83 centimeters long, but its average length is no more than 45 cm.

Habitat

This eel lives in lairs on the sandy bottom, at depths of from five to about 100 meters.

Distribution

Gulf of Aqaba, Red Sea.

Biology and Behavior

A gregarious species. Each eel lives in a tube dug out of the sand a short distance from the others. They are quick to hide as soon as they sense danger and catch plankton by undulating in a vertical position, with more than half their body buried in the sand.

Red Sea Garden Eel

Gorgasia sillneri

13

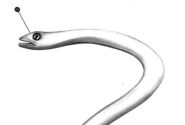

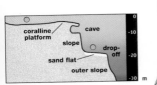

coralline platform
cave
slope
drop-off
sand flat
outer slope
0
-10
-20
-30 m

COMMENTS

The "walls" of their lairs are cemented with mucus produced by a special gland at the end of their tail.

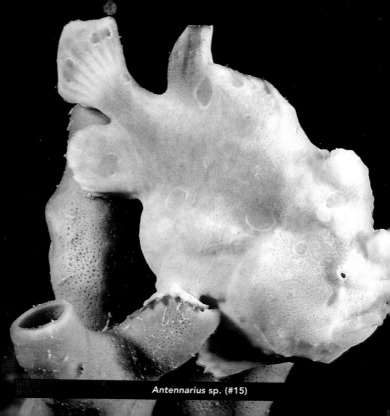

Antennarius sp. (#15)

LIZARDFISHES FROGFISHES

Lizardfishes belong to the **Synodontidae** family and owe their name to the fact that, as is the case with terrestrial lizards, they love to remain immobile for long periods. Their cylindrical bodies taper at the caudal end and are 14-32 centimeters long. Their fins have no spines. Voracious predators despite their tiny size, they have a large, deep mouth with numerous long, thin teeth and feed mainly on small fish, which they attack with sudden lunges. Frogfishes belong to the **Antennariidae** family and are rarer than lizardfishes and much more difficult to spot because of their capacity to camouflage themselves. Antennariidae are small (5-27 cm), globular in shape and have loose, slightly spinous skin. Their cranium has markedly protruding jaws and the mouth is very large. Their first dorsal spine, immediately above the mouth, is a long stalk-like appendage with a sort of lure at its end; remaining immobile, the frogfish moves this stalk, attracting small fish, which they swallow whole. The females are oviparous and lay hundreds of eggs wrapped in a gelatinous mass that float in the water.

Common genera in the Red Sea:
Synodus, Saurida, Antennarius.

57

Common Lizardfish

Synodus variegatus (Lacepède, 1803)

I **Pesce lucertola variegato**
D **Eidechsenfisch**
F **Poisson-lézard bigarré**

25 cm

3-50 m

Description

An elongate body that is flat ventrally and tapering toward the tail. The head is wide, the mouth faces upward and the eyes are set high, almost dorsal. The body is brown or reddish, with differently colored spots. Maximum length 25 cm.

Habitat

It lives in lagoons and on the exposed side of reefs at depths of as much as 50 meters.

Distribution

Widespread in the Red Sea and the Indo-Pacific region as far as Micronesia.

Biology and Behavior

The common lizardfish prefers hard substrata but can camouflage itself in the sand. It waits for its prey by raising itself on its pectoral fins and attacks it with a sudden lunge. It feeds mostly on smaller fishes, which it captures when they pass by.

Common Lizardfish

Synodus variegatus

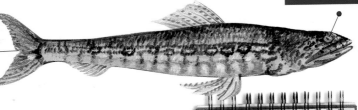

coralline platform
cave
slope
drop-off
sand flat
outer slope

0
-10
-20
-30 m

COMMENTS
It remains immobile and alone on the reef, even for hours, waiting for its prey.

15 Freckled Frogfish

Antennarius coccineus (Lesson, 1831)

I **Pesce rana (Antennario)**
D **Anglerfisch**
F **Antennaire moucheté**

 13 cm

 1-75 m

AULOPIFORMES

Antennariidae

Description
Fish with a globular body that is flat ventrally. The wide mouth faces upward. The first ray of the dorsal spine has become a stalk-like appendage used to lure prey. It uses its short pectoral fins to drag itself on the floor. It can camouflage itself very well thanks to the many warty protuberances and its color, which varies from red to yellowish in different individuals. Maximum length 13 cm.

Habitat
The freckled frogfish lives in lagoons and cliff water holes but also on exposed coral flats, from the surface to a depth of 75 m.

Distribution
Red Sea and Indo-Pacific region.

Biology and Behavior
A voracious predator, it waits for its victims by remaining motionless on the bottom and snatching them with its extremely expandable mouths.

Freckled Frogfish

Antennarius coccineus

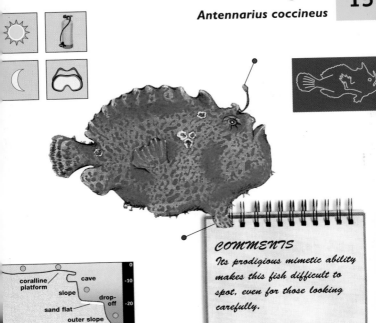

15

COMMENTS

Its prodigious mimetic ability makes this fish difficult to spot, even for those looking carefully.

coralline platform

cave

slope

drop-off

sand flat

outer slope

Sargocentron spiniferum (#17)

SOLDIERFISHES SQUIRRELFISHES

Soldierfishes and squirrelfishes belong to the **Holocentridae** family, which has eight genera and about 60 species, and are the most typical nocturnal reef predators. It must be said that most zoologists divide the Holocentridae into two sub-families: Myripristinae, or soldierfishes, and Holocentrinae, squirrelfishes.

During the day these fishes live secluded in the caves and crevices of the reef, while at sunset they go out to look for food. Their red color makes them almost totally invisible and their large eyes are quite adapted to seeing well at night.

The soldierfishes, of the *Myripristis* genus, are small, have a pointed snout, feed mostly on plankton which they find at night in the open sea, and generally live in schools.

Squirrelfishes, most of which belong to the genus *Sargocentron*, are larger and their dorsal fins have robust rays. They have long spines around the operculi (unlike soldierfishes, which have no spines). They are territorial and rather solitary creatures that feed on small fish, crustaceans and worms.

Common genera in the Red Sea:
Myripristis, Neoniphon, Sargocentron.

White-Edged Soldierfish

Myripristis murdjan (Forsskål, 1775)

- I **Pesce soldato**
- D **Weißsaum-Soldatenfisch**
- F **Poisson-soldat à œillères**

 23 cm

2-37 m

Description

This fish has an oval, robust body and large eyes and its mouth face slightly upward. The caudal fin is clearly forked. Red coloration, with the anterior margin of the second dorsal fin and the ventral, anal and caudal fins white. Maximum length 23 cm.

Habitat

It lives in lagoons and on the outer slope of the coral reef, hidden crevices, at a depth of as much as 37 meters.

Distribution

Red Sea and Indo-Pacific region.

Biology and Behavior

It congregates in small groups in the reef crevices by day. It is a nocturnal predator and moves toward the open sea to capture planktonic crustaceans. During the reproductive period this soldierfish forms couples that court by going up to the surface, where they separate and the eggs are fertilized.

White-Edged Soldierfish

Myripristis murdjan

16

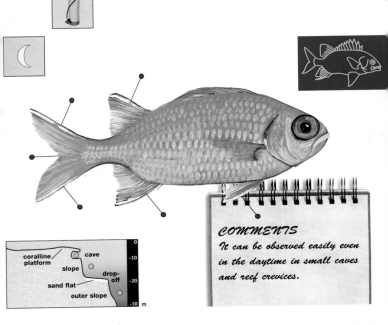

COMMENTS

It can be observed easily even in the daytime in small caves and reef crevices.

coralline platform

cave

slope

drop-off

sand flat

outer slope

0
-10
-20
-30 m

Sabre Squirrelfish

Sargocentron spiniferum (Forsskål, 1775)

I **Pesce scoiattolo spinoso**
D **Riesenhusar**
F **Marignan géant**

 45 cm

5-120 m

Description

Body tall and compressed, dorsal profile of head concave, the mouth facing upward because of the longer lower jaw.

The tail is clearly forked. A venomous spine is on the operculum.

The color of this fish is red, but the edge of the scales is white and the fins are yellowish. Maximum length 45 cm.

Habitat

Coral sea floors rich in crevices, up to a depth of 120 meters.

Distribution

Red Sea and Indo-Pacific region as far as Japan and Micronesia.

Biology and Behavior

A solitary, nocturnal species that spends the day in the reef crevices or under madrepore platforms.

It feeds mainly on fish and crustaceans, as well as a great variety of other invertebrates.

Sabre Squirrelfish

Sargocentron spiniferum

min   max
index of dangerousness

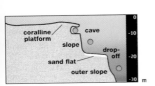

COMMENTS

The largest of the 26 species
in this genus. It can be seen
by day in the reef caves, and
at sunset it comes out to look
for food.

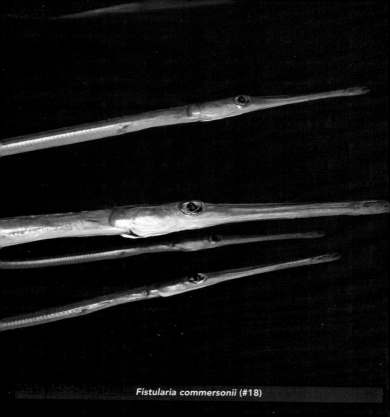

Fistularia commersonii (#18)

CORNETFISHES
NEEDLEFISHES

ornetfishes, which are also called trumpetfishes or flute-fishes, belong to the **Fistulariidae** family, a word deriving from the Latin *fistula*, or reed. They have an elongate, cylindrical body that is greenish-grey that ends in a long filament. Their extremely long snout and small mouth allow these fishes to poke about among the madrepores to feed on small fish or crustaceans. Cornetfishes live near the coral reef, on the sand flats and also in the open sea, at varying depths, sometimes in groups of dozens. Needlefishes are quite similar. They belong to the **Belonidae** family (from the Greek *belon*, or needle). They are silvery-greenish, with a more slender body than the cornetfishes and with the dorsal and anal fins in a more posterior position. The Belonidae also have a very long mouth that is like a kind of beak with numerous thin teeth. Needlefishes live near the surface, where they are camouflaged among the light reflections and the waves, waiting for small pelagic fishes to pass by. When they are frightened, these fishes may jump out of the water, especially at night.

Common genera in the Red Sea:
Fistularia, Tylosurus.

Cornetfish (Flutemouth)

Fistularia commersonii (Rüppell, 1838)

I **Pesce trombetta**
D **Flötenfisch**
F **Fistulaire de Commerson**

150 cm

1-100 m

SYNGNATHIFORMES

Fistulariidae

Description

An extremely elongated, cylindrical body that is depressed laterally, with a thin, tubular mouth. The dorsal and anal fins are in a very posterior position; the small, forked caudal fin has a long median filament. Dorsally, the cornetfish is olive green, while the underbody is silvery. Maximum length 150 cm.

Habitat

This fish lives in detrital zones or those rich in madrepores, from the surface to near the bottom.

Distribution

Red Sea and Indo-Pacific region.

Biology and Behavior

It feeds on small fish, crustaceans or cephalopods, which it sucks violently into its long mouth. It often lies in wait near large madrepores, either alone or in groups. It may also mingle with other fish while hunting for food, using them to hide from its prey.

Cornetfish (Flutemouth)

Fistularia commersonii

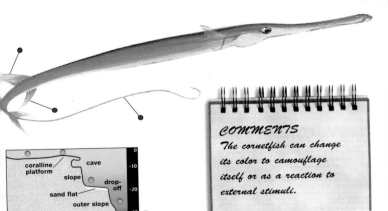

COMMENTS

The cornetfish can change its color to camouflage itself or as a reaction to external stimuli.

coralline platform
cave
slope
drop-off
sand flat
outer slope

0
-10
-20
-30 m

BELONIFORMES

Belonidae

Red Sea Needlefish

Tylosurus choram (Rüppell, 1837)

I **Aguglia del Mar Rosso**
D **Rotmeer-Hornhecht**
F **Orphie de Mer Rouge**

120 cm

0-5 m

Description

A needlefish with a cylindrical body tapering at the ends and a very long and thin mouth. It has one triangular dorsal fin on a level with the anal fin. The tail is slightly forked. It is green dorsally and silvery on its sides and ventrally.

Maximum length 120 cm.

Habitat

The Red Sea needlefish lives on the surface of open waters or on coralline bottoms.

Distribution

It was once endemic to the Red Sea and Gulf of Oman, but since the opening of the Suez Canal has also lived in the Mediterranean.

Biology and Behavior

A fine swimmer able to go for long distances, even in the open sea. It stays close to the surface to hide from its prey, which consists of small fish which its pierces with its long, sword-like mouth.

Red Sea Needlefish

Tylosurus choram

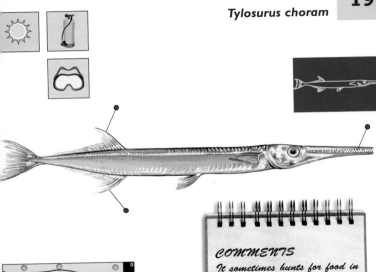

COMMENTS
It sometimes hunts for food in groups. It has very sharp teeth.

coralline platform
cave
slope
drop-off
sand flat
outer slope

0
-10
-20
-30 m

Pterois miles (#20)

LIONFISHES STONEFISHES CROCODILEFISHES

ionfishes and stonefishes belong to the **Scorpenidae** family, which is characterized by a long, spinous head with bony crests on the cheeks, as well as by venomous spines. The most common and representative species of this family are lionfishes (genus *Pterois*)—sometimes erroneously called scorpionfishes—and stonefishes genus *Synanceia*), and the false stonefishes (genus *Scorpaenopsis*), also sometimes called scorpionfishes. Lionfishes, so named for their elegant fins in the shape of a mane, are good swimmers and are active mostly at night, while they usually rest during the day in reef crevices and caves. Stonefishes and the devil scorpionfish are solitary creatures that swim very little and prefer to camouflage themselves on the sea bottom while waiting for their prey. All Scorpaenidae are timid and not aggressive, but they are also extremely dangerous, and even lethal, if they are touched since they have a powerful poison that causes respiratory paralysis and cardiac arrest. The innocuous crocodile fish, which spends most of its time half-hidden on the sandy bottom, belongs to the **Platycephalidae** family (Scorpaeniformes order).

Common genera in the Red Sea:
Pterois, Synanceia, Scorpaenopsis, Papilloculiceps.

Lionfish

Pterois miles (Bennet, 1828)

I **Pesce leone**
D **Rotfeuerfisch**
F **Rascasse volante commune**

38 cm

2-55 m

Description

A tall, robust body characterized by the feathery appearance of the dorsal fin and the wing-like pectoral fin. The dorsal fin is supported by long, spinous rays connected to venom-bearing glands. The lionfish is brown, with thin, vertical white and reddish stripes. Related species: *Pterois radiata, P. volitans.*

Habitat

This fish prefers areas with many crevices in lagoons or on the outer slope of coral reefs up to a depth of 55 meters. It is often found in caves or among rubble.

Distribution

Red Sea and Indian Ocean (Maldives).

Biology and Behavior

This fish is nocturnal and spends the day in sheltered, shady places where it may stay in groups. It feeds on small fish and crustaceans, which it captures with its fins and swallows quickly.

Lionfish

Pterois miles

min   max

index of dangerousness

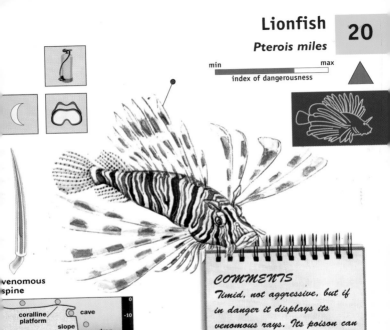

venomous spine

coralline platform

cave

slope

drop-off

sand flat

outer slope

0

-10

-20

-30 m

COMMENTS

Timid, not aggressive, but if in danger it displays its venomous rays. Its poison can be lethal.

Stonefish

Synanceia verrucosa Bloch & Schneider, 1801

I **Pesce pietra**
D **Steinfisch**
F **Poisson-pierre**

40 cm

1-30 m

Description

This fish has an extraordinary natural camouflage in its yellowish brown color and warty skin. A large head with an almost vertical mouth and eyes in a dorsal position. The dorsal fin is supported b spinous rays connected to a venomous gland.
Maximum length 40 cm.

Habitat

It lives in detrital or coralline bottoms at a maximum depth of 3C meters.

Distribution

Red Sea and Indo-Pacific region.

Biology and Behavior

The stonefish is a solitary creature that waits motionless on the bottom for its prey (fish and crustaceans) to pass by. It blends in perfectly with the environment and can even cover itself with sand or algae, so that it is invisible even to those who look carefully for it.

Stonefish

Synanceia verrucosa

min _____ max
index of dangerousness

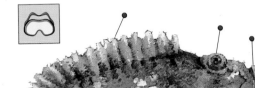

venomous spine

coralline platform
cave
slope
sand flat
drop-off
outer slope

0
-10
-20
-30 m

COMMENTS
Despite its apparently tame behavior, its poison can be lethal for humans.

Devil Scorpionfish

Scorpaenopsis diabolus Cuvier, 1829

I **Falso pesce pietra**
D **Falscher Steinfisch**
F **Rascasse diable**

30 cm

1-70 m

Description

The devil scorpionfish has a globular body flattened ventrally and with a doral hump. The head is large, with a wide, upward-facing mouth. The pectoral fins are wide, rounded and kept outspread when the fish is lying on the sea bottom. Brown or reddish mimetic coloration. Maximum length 30 cm. Related species: *S. oxycephala*.

Habitat

It lives in lagoon areas and on seaward reefs up to a depth of 70 m. It prefers detrital, sandy or rocky environments, where it is perfectly camouflaged.

Distribution

This species is widespread in the Red Sea and in the Indo-Pacific region as far as Micronesia.

Biology and Behavior

It waits motionless for its prey on the bottom. If disturbed, it raises its yellow pectoral fins as a warning.

Devil Scorpionfish

Scorpaenopsis diabolus

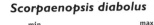

min   max
index of dangerousness

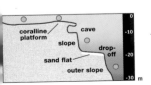

COMMENTS

Its venomous glands lie at the base of the spinous rays of the dorsal fin. Its sting is quite painful.

Crocodilefish

Papilloculiceps longiceps (Cuvier. 1829)

I **Pesce coccodrillo**
D **Teppich-Krokodilsfisch**
F **Poisson crocodile**

70 cm

1-30 m

SCORPAENIFORMES

Platycephalidae

Description

The crocodilefish has a flat, rhomboidal body with a triangular hea
and a wide, upward-facing mouth, as well as two dorsal fins.

Its eyes are large and dorsal, covered by ragged eyelids. It ha
mimetic coloration: grey and greenish-brown, with darker spots.

Habitat

It lives on sandy or detrital bottoms and crevices, from the surfac
to a depth of 30 meters.

Distribution

The Red Sea and the eastern coast of Africa as far as Madagascar.

Biology and Behavior

This fish is a predator that remains hidden on the bottom, lying i
wait for fish and crustaceans. It is a solitary species rarely seen i
couples and often found near rubble. Despite its threatening look, i
is absolutely innocuous.

Papilloculiceps longiceps

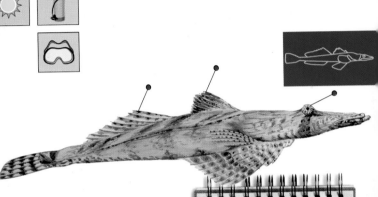

COMMENTS
If threatened, it tends to remain immobile on the bottom and then swims away with curious lateral movements of its body.

coralline platform | cave
slope | drop-off
sand flat
outer slope

0
-10
-20
-30 m

Variola louti (#29)

GROUPERS - ANTHIAS

Despite their obvious morphological differences, both groupers and the small anthias belong to the same large **Serranidae** family, which is distinguished by the presence of a long dorsal fin with well developed spines and small spines on the operculi. Groupers are quite varied in size, and some species are truly enormous, weighing over 300 kilograms. They are solitary, spending the day in coral reef cavities or hidden among madrepores and at sunset coming out in search of food. Groupers are fearsome, voracious predators, feeding mostly on fish. They are protogynous hermaphrodites, that is, females at birth that later become males. They change the color of their bodies when passing from the juvenile to the adult stage and can also do so temporarily, according to the circumstances (depth of water, mood, etc.). The highly colored anthias, which are much smaller than groupers (maximum length 15 cm) are the most common and typical reef fishes. They live in large schools. The males are violet, while the females are orange and can become males if need be in order to guarantee the right ratio between males and females, which is about 1:8.

Common genera in the Red Sea: *Aethaloperca, Cephalopholis, Epinephelus, Variola, Plectropomus, Pseudanthias, Pseudochromis.*

Coral Grouper

Cephalopholis miniata (Forsskål, 1775)

I **Cernia corallina**
D **Juwelenzackenbarsch**
F **Mérou rouge**

40 cm

2-150 m

PERCIFORMES

Serranidae

Description

A tapering body with a convex dorsal profile and pointed head. The edges of the fins are rounded. The body color varies from red to orange, but can change to lighter vertical stripes on the sides. Thick blue punctation covers the body and fins. Maximum length 40 cm.

Habitat

Widespread along the seaward slope of the reef up to 150 meters' depth.

Distribution

Common in the entire Indo-Pacific region, from the Red Sea to Micronesia.

Biology and Behavior

The coral grouper feeds on fish and crustaceans. The males have harems of 2-12 females, who defend their territory. The females attain sexual maturity when they are 25 cm long. The juveniles are entirely orange and live sheltered among the corals

Coral Grouper

Cephalopholis miniata

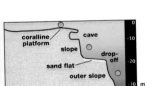

coralline platform · cave · slope · drop-off · sand flat · outer slope

0
-10
-20
-30 m

COMMENTS

A hermaphroditic species with sexual inversion from female to male.

Redmouth Grouper

Aethaloperca rogaa (Forsskål, 1775)

I **Cernia bocca rossa**
D **Rotmaul-Zackenbarsch**
F **Mérou gueule rouge**

60 cm

5-60 m

PERCIFORMES

Description

This species, named after the red or orange color of the inside of its mouth, has a characteristic compressed shape and is tall anteriorly. The profile of the head is convex, with an upward-facing pointed mouth. Tail truncated. Body brown or black. Maximum length 60 cm.

Habitat

It lives in crevices among corals up to 60 meters' depth. It can also be found at the base of large gorgonians (genus *Subergorgia*).

Distribution

Widespread in the Red Sea and along the eastern coast of Africa, it is present also in the entire Indo-Pacific region.

Biology and Behavior

This species makes rapid raids among schools of glassfishes. Its diet also includes other fish and crustaceans.

There is sexual inversion from female to male and it can reproduce all year long.

Serranidae

Redmouth Grouper

Aethaloperca rogaa

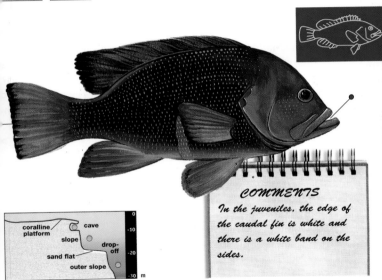

COMMENTS

In the juveniles, the edge of the caudal fin is white and there is a white band on the sides.

coralline platform

cave

slope

drop-off

sand flat

outer slope

0

-10

-20

-30 m

Blacktip Grouper

Epinephelus fasciatus (Forsskål, 1775)

I **Cernia a punte nere**
D **Baskenmützenzackenbarsch**
F **Mérou pointes noires**

40 cm

4-160 m

PERCIFORMES

Description

A tapering body that is convex dorsally, with a pointed head. The edges of the fins are rounded. The tail is wide and rounded but closes like a fan when the fish is immobile on the bottom.

The color of this grouper varies from light pink to orange. A broad, darker spot covers its eyes and forehead. It may also have light vertical stripes. Maximum length 40 cm.

Habitat

It lives on sandy or coralline bottoms up to 160 meters' depth.

Distribution

Quite common the Red Sea and entire Indo-Pacific region.

Biology and Behavior

It feeds on fish, crustaceans, cephalopods and other invertebrates. It sometimes gathers into small groups of 10-15. The juveniles sometimes find shelter in mangrove swamps.

Serranidae

Epinephelus fasciatus

COMMENTS
Fished by the Bedouin. There is also a variant with a uniformly pale body except in the frontal portion.

coralline platform
cave
slope
drop-off
sand flat
outer slope

Malabar Grouper

Epinephelus malabaricus (Bloch & Schneider, 1801)

I **Cernia di Malabar**
D **Malabarzackenbarsch**
F **Mérou Malabar**

120 cm

2-60 m

Description

A large grouper that may be as long as 1.2 meters and weigh up to 150 kilograms. Its body is elongate and massive, with a broad, rounded tail. The body is marmorized, lighter on the back and head, with grey and white spots. There is thick punctation on the entire body. Related species: *E. fuscoguttatus*.

Habitat

This species adapts to various environments: lagoons, mangrove swamps, sand bottoms, reefs. It goes as deep as 60 meters.

Distribution

Typical species of the Red Sea and east African coast; Indo-Pacific region as far as Japan and Australia.

Biology and Behavior

A voracious predator, it feeds on fish, crustaceans and, occasionally, cephalopods. The juveniles live in lagoons or brackish waters.

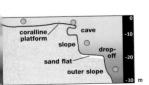

COMMENTS
A hermaphroditic species that changes from female to male.

28 Arabian Grouper

Epinephelus tauvina (Forsskål, 1775)

I **Cernia maculata**
D **Braunfleckenzackenbarsch**
F **Mérou loutre**

70 cm

1-50 m

Description

This grouper has an elongate, massive body and a large head with a wide, upward-facing mouth. Its eyes are located in front of the mouth. The edges of the fins are rounded and dark. The body has characteristic, broad grey and whitish patches, with smaller black or reddish spots.

Habitat

It lives from the surface to a depth of 50 meters on the outer margin of the reef. It also frequents lagoons and brackish waters.

Distribution

Widespread in the tropical and subtropical areas of the Red Sea and in the entire Indo-Pacific region.

Biology and Behavior

The Arabian grouper feeds almost exclusively on fish. The juveniles are frequently seen in shallow lagoons, where they may be trapped when the tide is low.

PERCIFORMES

Serranidae

Arabian Grouper

Epinephelus tauvina

28

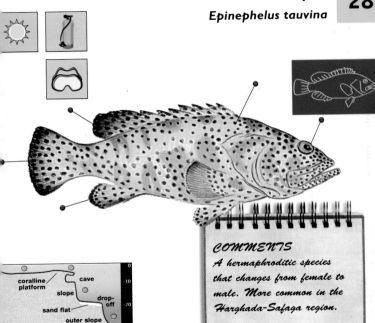

COMMENTS

A hermaphroditic species that changes from female to male. More common in the Harghada-Safaga region.

coralline platform
cave
slope
drop-off
sand flat
outer slope

Moon Grouper

Variola louti (Forsskål, 1775)

I   **Cernia dalla coda a mezza luna**
D   **Mondflossenzackenbarsch**
F   **Mérou croissant jaune**

80 cm

3-250 m

Description

The moon grouper's body is tapering, with a rounded head an
upward-facing mouth. The tail is strongly crescent-shaped. The edge
of the fins are long and pointed. Its color varies from red-violet t
orange, with thick blue or pink punctation. The edges of the fins ar
yellow. Maximum length 80 cm.

Habitat

The seaward side of the reef, at a depth of 3-250 meters.

Distribution

Widespread in the entire Indo-Pacific region.

Biology and Behavior

A solitary species that chooses territories not frequented by othe
groupers. It feeds mostly on fish and crustaceans. It is hermaphro
ditic, changing from female to male during its lifetime.

Moon Grouper

Variola louti

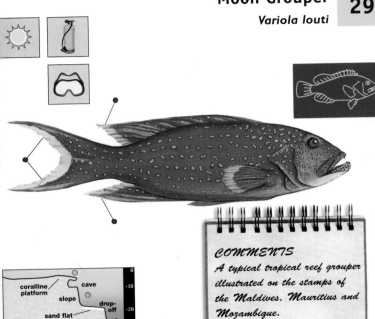

COMMENTS

A typical tropical reef grouper illustrated on the stamps of the Maldives, Mauritius and Mozambique.

coralline platform

cave

slope

sand flat

drop-off

outer slope

0

-10

-20

-30 m

Scalefin Anthias

Pseudanthias squamipinnis (Peters, 1855)

I   **Anthias**
D   **Haremsfahnenbarsch**
F   **Barbier bijou**

15 cm

1-35 m

PERCIFORMES

Description

Its body is oval, with a regular, pointed snout. The crescent-shaped tail has elongated margins in the males (♂), which can be recognized by their fuchsia body with a golden sheen and the long third ray of the dorsal fin. The females (♀) are orange, with a violet mask on the forehead and eyes. Maximum length 15 cm.

Habitat

The scalefin anthias lives wherever there are rich coralline formations, up to a depth of 35 meters.

Distribution

Red Sea and Indo-Pacific region.

Biology and Behavior

A diurnal species that is very gregarious, forming large schools around reefs in order to take refuge there if threatened.

It is territorial and consists of harems dominated by one male. It feeds on plankton.

Serranidae

Scalefin Anthias

Pseudanthias squamipinnis

♂

♀

coralline
platform

cave

slope

sand flat

drop-
off

outer slope

0
-10
-20
-30 m

COMMENTS
When the male dies, the
dominating female changes sex.
Reproduction occurs at sunset,
in December–February in the
Red Sea.

Red Sea Fairy Basslet

Anthias taeniatus Klunzinger, 1884

I **Anthias striato**
D **Rotmeer-Fahnenbarsch**
F **Barbier de Mer Rouge**

13 cm

10-40 m

Description

The body is oval and regular. The crescent-shaped tail has pointed margins. The males are reddish, white ventrally and have a whitish stripe on the sides. The females are orange and their lateral stripes are pinkish. Maximum length 13 cm.

Habitat

It lives on coralline bottoms at a depth of 10-40 meters.

Distribution

An endemic species of the Red Sea.

Biology and Behavior

The Red Sea fairy basslet gathers in large schools along the reef slope and near coralline formations.

It is a diurnal species, is territorial and feeds only on zooplankton. It forms harems dominated by a single male.

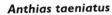

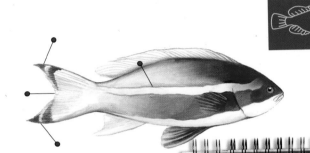

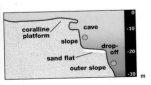

coralline platform
cave
slope
drop-off
sand flat
outer slope
0
-10
-20
-30
m

COMMENTS
The dominating female changes sex when the male dies and governs the harem in its place.

Priacanthus hamrur (#32)

BIGEYES
CARDINALFISHES

Bigeyes belong to the **Priacanthidae** family and are typical nocturnal fishes, as can be seen in their well developed ocular apparatus, after which this species was named. Other features of the Priacanthids are their compressed bodies, very large mouths and continuous dorsal fin. During the day, they live in the caves and crevices of the coral reef, while they go into the open sea at night in search of their food, zooplankton.

Cardinalfishes are part of the **Apogonidae** family, a large group of fishes represented mostly by the genus *Apogon*, which has 39 species. They are small, with an elongate body about 10 cm long, two dorsal fins and large eyes.

Like the bigeyes, these fish feed at night on zooplankton, while during the day they often gather in sedentary groups under the branches of acropores. During the reproduction season (late spring-summer) the females mate, lay their eggs (about 3,000) and the males, after having fertilized the eggs, keep them in their mouths for about one week, until the fry hatch.

Common genera in the Red Sea:
Priacanthus, Apogon, Cheilodipterus.

Common Bigeye

Priacanthus hamrur (Forsskål, 1775)

I **Pesce occhio grosso**
D **Großaugensoldat**
F **Priacanthe commun**

40 cm

8-250 m

PERCIFORMES

Description

An oval, compressed body with a thin caudal stalk and a truncate or slightly concave tail. The head is pointed and the mouth faces upward because of the greater length of the lower jaw.

The coloration is reddish brown. Maximum length 40 cm.

Habitat

The common bigeye lives in caves in the outer reef slope, at a depth of 8-250 meters.

Distribution

Red Sea and the Indo-Pacific region as far as Easter Island.

Biology and Behavior

A nocturnal species that hides in the coralline crevices during the day. Here it may congregate in rather large groups. It feeds on small fish, cephalopods and crustaceans.

Priacanthidae

Common Bigeye

Priacanthus hamrur

COMMENTS

Its daytime coloration differs from the noctural one, which has silvery stripes. Illustrated on Israeli stamps.

coralline platform

cave

slope

drop-off

sand flat

outer slope

0
-10
-20
-30 m

Eyeshadow Cardinalfish

Apogon exostigma (Jordan & Starks, 1906)

I **Pesce cardinale dall'occhio striato**
D **Irisierender-Kardinalbarsch**
F **Apogon iridescent**

10 cm

2-40 m

PERCIFORMES

Description

The body is tapering, with a slightly forked tail that has rounded edges. Two dorsal fins on a level with the ventral and anal fins. The coloration is whitish and iridescent. A black streak runs from the mouth to the tail, also covering the eyes. A black spot is on the caudal stalk. Maximum length 10 cm. Related species: *Apogon annularis, A. aureus, A. nigrofasciatus*.

Habitat

It lives in protected reef zones, at a depth of 12-40 meters.

Distribution

Red Sea and entire Indo-Pacific region.

Biology and Behavior

The eyeshadow cardinalfish is a timid nocturnal species that is often seen near coralline formations, where it takes refuge if threatened. It swims near the bottom in search of invertebrates and small fish.

Apogonidae

Eyeshadow Cardinalfish

Apogon exostigma

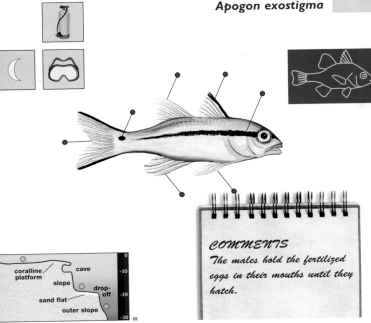

COMMENTS

The males hold the fertilized eggs in their mouths until they hatch.

coralline platform

cave

slope

drop-off

sand flat

outer slope

0

-10

-20

-30 m

Plectorhinchus gaterinus (#34)

GRUNTS – BREAMS

Grunts, which are sometimes called "sweetlips," belong to the **Haemulidae** family, which comprises the genera *Plectorinchus* and *Diagramma*. Haemulids are average-sized fish with very thick lips (hence one of their common names), a mouth with small conical teeth, and a continuous dorsal fin. Their other name derives from the fact that they sometimes make grunt-like noises. The juveniles of some species, in their transition to the adult stage, change their coloration, which is very bright and has patterns. These fishes are active mostly at night, when they leave their refuges in the reef (by day they can often be spotted in their shelters in caves and rubble) to feed on small invertebrates. They are solitary creatures, especially the juveniles, but also congregate in large schools, sometimes mingling with butterflyfishes. Breams belong to the **Sparidae** family and are distinguished by their massive body with medium- or large-size scales that is similar to that of the Lujtanidae. They are solitary or congregate in small schools and live in sheltered waters, feeding on echinoderms (sea urchins) and other invertebrates.

Common genera in the Red Sea:
Plectorhinchus, Diagramma, Acanthopagrus.

Black-Spotted Grunt

Plectorhinchus gaterinus (Forsskål, 1775)

I **Grugnitore maculato**
D **Schwarzgepunktete Süßlippe**
F **Lippu gaterin**

45 cm

5-55 m

PERCIFORMES

Description

This grunt has a tapering body with a convex dorsal profile which i
higher in the anterior portion. Its caudal fin is truncate. It has
whitish or silvery body, while the fins and lips are yellow. Severa
black spots cover the sides and median fins. Maximum length 45 cm

Habitat

It lives on coralline bottoms along the seaward edge of the reef, at
depth of 5-55 meters. It may visit sandy lagoons and estuaries.

Distribution

Widespread in the Red Sea and the western Indian Ocean. Its presence in the Seychelles Islands is still being debated.

Biology and Behavior

This is a nocturnal species that feeds on fish and crustaceans. It
spends the day sheltered in small groups under umbrella-like
coralline formations.

Haemulidae

Black-Spotted Grunt

Plectorhinchus gaterinus

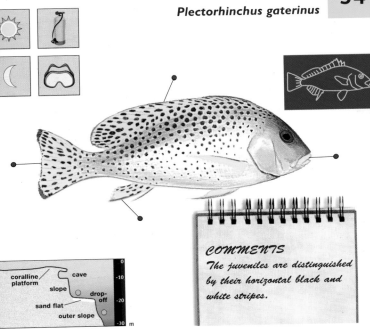

COMMENTS
The juveniles are distinguished by their horizontal black and white stripes.

coralline platform
cave
slope
drop-off
sand flat
outer slope

0
-10
-20
-30 m

Doublebar Bream

Acanthopagrus bifasciatus (Forsskål, 1775)

- I **Orata del Mar Rosso**
- D **Zweibandbrasse**
- F **Pagre à deux bandes**

50 cm

2-20 m

Description

The body of this bream is robust and compressed, taller in the ant rior portion. The head is short with a sharply inclined upper prof and subterminal mouth. The tail is forked and the dorsal fin is su ported by spinous rays. It is silvery on its sides; the dorsal and caud fins are yellow, while the ventral and anal ones are black. Two wid vertical black bands cover its eyes and operculum.
Maximum length 50 cm.

Habitat

The doublebar bream likes sandy or coralline floors, at a depth of 20 meters. It also frequents lagoon zones.

Distribution

The Red Sea, Persian Gulf and the eastern coast of Africa.

Biology and Behavior

A solitary or slightly gregarious species. It feeds on invertebrat (above all crustaceans and mollusks). It lays small floating eggs.

Doublebar Bream

Acanthopagrus bifasciatus

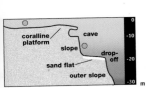

coralline platform

cave

slope

drop-off

sand flat

outer slope

0
-10
-20
-30 m

COMMENTS

It is often seen in groups of 4-8 in shallow water on the reef slope, sometimes together with emperorfishes and snappers.

Platax orbicularis (#36)

BATFISHES

The name of these fishes derives from their highly developed dorsal and anal fins, which, especially in the juveniles, reminds one of two wings. Batfishes belong to the **Ephippidae** family. These are average-size fishes (their maximum length is 50 centimeters) with a tall, flat body covered by tiny scales, a small and protruding mouth with brush-like teeth. Although they are much larger than butterflyfishes, they are similar in their habits and disk-like shape. Batfishes are omnivorous but prefer algae and small invertebrates. They usually live in couples or in groups, sometimes schools with hundreds of individuals, and are often sedentary in the vicinity of the outer reef slope.

Small groups or couples are usually seen resting in the reef shelters or near madrepore towers. Since they are curious creatures, divers can get quite close to them.

At times, especially in the case of juveniles, batfishes live among mangrove roots and lie on one side in order to resemble dead leaves. These fishes are caught not for their meat but because they are very popular among aquarium owners.

Common genera in the Red Sea:
Platax.

Batfish

Platax orbicularis (Forsskål, 1775)

- I **Pesce pipistrello**
- D **Schwarmfledermausfisch**
- F **Platax orbiculaire**

50 cm

5-30 m

Description

An extremely compressed disk-shaped body whose very tall anal fin and dorsal fin make it look almost triangular. A pointed, slightly concave head and truncate tail rounded in the middle. It is silvery, the unpaired fins have black borders, and the ventral fins are yellowish. Two dark vertical bands cover the eyes and operculum. Maximum length 50 cm. Related species: *Phalax teira*.

Habitat

The open sea opposite the outer reef slope at a depth of 5-30 meters, or lagoons.

Distribution

Red Sea and entire Indo-Pacific region.

Biology and Behavior

Often gregarious, frequenting very different environments. It lives among rubble and sometimes settles below madrepore formations. Its diet consists of algae, invertebrates and small fish.

COMMENTS The juveniles have very long fins and resemble floating mangrove leaves due to their color and movement. P. teria has a black spot in front of the anal fin.

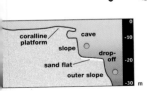

coralline platform
cave
slope
drop-off
sand flat
outer slope

0
-10
-20
-30 m

Lutjanus monostigma (#39)

SNAPPERS

These fishes, which the Arabs call *bohar*, belong to the large **Lutjanidae** family, which has twenty genera that live in all tropical and subtropical seas. Snappers are from average- to large-sized (some species are more than a meter long) and have a continuous dorsal fin with rays that are hard anteriorly and soft posteriorly. Their body is covered with large scales and they have robust, prominent teeth, hence their name. Snappers prey on crustaceans and fish smaller than they, but some species feed on zooplankton. There are 14 species of Lutjanidae in the Red Sea, which live in the immediate vicinity of the reef at different depths; they may congregate in schools with hundreds of fish that often include members of other families, such as butterflyfishes.

Snappers never rest on the sea bottom, as the Serranidae sometimes do, but move around continuously in compact formations. Schools of snappers are often sedentary and tend to return to the same places along the reef.

These fishes are very important commercially since their meat is highly prized and very popular throughout the world.

Common genera in the Red Sea:
Lutjanus, Paracaesio, Macolor, Aprion.

Twinspot Snapper

Lutjanus bohar Forsskål, 1775

I **Dentice bimaculato**
D **Zweifleckschnapper**
F **Vivaneau à deux taches**

90 cm

10-180 m

Description

This snapper has a robust, tapering body with a regularly-shaped head. The caudal fin is slightly forked. It is reddish-brown and somewhat darker dorsally; the fins are dark but the pectoral fins are pinkish. Maximum length 90 cm, weight 13 kilograms.

Habitat

It lives in lagoons or on reef slopes up to a depth of 180 meters.

Distribution

Red Sea and Indo-Pacific region. It is more common in the vicinity of islands rather than in continental waters.

Biology and Behavior

A tendentially solitary species.

It hunts by night, feeding mainly on fish, which it captures with swift movements. Its diet also includes crustaceans and other invertebrates. It seems able to breed all year long.

Twinspot Snapper

Lutjanus bohar

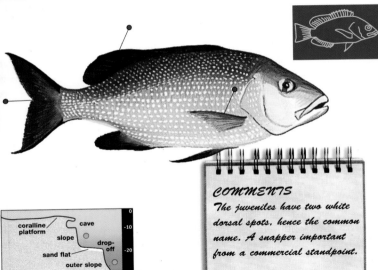

COMMENTS

The juveniles have two white dorsal spots, hence the common name. A snapper important from a commercial standpoint.

coralline platform
cave
slope
drop-off
sand flat
outer slope

0
-10
-20
-30 m

Humpback Snapper

Lutjanus gibbus (Forsskål, 1775)

- I **Azzannatore gobbo**
- D **Buckel-Schnapper**
- F **Vivaneau bossu**

50 cm

2-150 m

PERCIFORMES

Description

A robust, compressed body that is taller in the anterior portion. The profile of the head is slightly convex. Its tail is forked, with rounded margins. The posterior lobes of the dorsal and anal fins are pointed. The body is red and darker dorsally. Maximum length 50 cm.

Habitat

This snapper is often seen on protected coralline bottoms. It lives at a depth of up to 150 meters.

Distribution

Red Sea and Indo-Pacific region, as far north as Japan and as far south as Australia.

Biology and Behavior

The humpback snapper forms large, compact schools that settle near the reef during the day. It is a nocturnal predator that feeds mainly on fish and various invertebrates, including crustaceans, cephalopods and echinoderms.

Lutjanidae

Humpback Snapper

Lutjanus gibbus

COMMENTS
It can be spotted mostly at drop-offs. At night it prefers to hunt alone or in couples.

coralline platform
cave
slope
drop-off
sand flat
outer slope
0
-10
-20
-30 m

Onespot Snapper

Lutjanus monostigma (Cuvier, 1828)

I **Azzannatore maculato**
D **Einfleckschnapper**
F **Vivaneau monotache**

60 cm

5-30 m

Description

The body of the onespot snapper is tapering, and convex dorsally. Its tail is slightly forked. It is yellow-silvery, sometimes pinkish, and the fins are yellow. There is a black spot along its sides on a level with the lateral line. Maximum length 60 cm.

Habitat

It lives in coralline areas with many shelters, at a maximum depth of 30 meters. It is often seen near caves or rubble.

Distribution

Red Sea and Indo-Pacific region as far as Australia and the Marquesas Islands.

Biology and Behavior

A solitary, or slightly gregarious, creature. Its diet consists of fish and crustaceans. It tends to be a nocturnal predator.

Onespot Snapper

Lutjanus monostigma

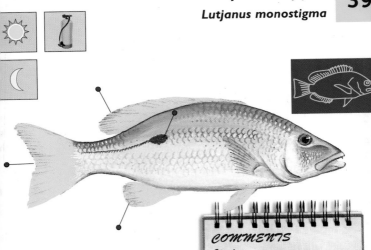

COMMENTS

If there are no caves or crevices available, it seeks shelter under tabular coral formations. Not easy to approach.

coralline platform
cave
slope
drop-off
sand flat
outer slope

0
-10
-20
-30 m

Caesio suevica (#41)

FUSILIERS

These fish belong to the **Caesionidae** family, from the Latin *caesius*, or greyish-blue. Fusiliers are often closely related to snappers, but can easily be distinguished from the latter by their smaller size (20-30 cm on an average), the shape of their snout, their elongate body and sharply forked tail.

Fusiliers have a greyish-blue body covered with tiny scales, a protactile mouth and a continuous dorsal fin.

They are quite widespread and live in large schools that move continuously, as swiftly as a bullet, often changing direction quickly. They can be spotted both near reefs and in the open sea, continuously on the move in search of zooplankton and often followed by predators such as barracuda and trevallies, from which they try to flee with their great speed and sudden changes of direction. Fusiliers sometimes rest at "cleaning stations" (see Cleaner Wrasses, page 203), waiting to feed on the organisms on the skin of other fishes.

Fusiliers are active by day and take shelter and rest at night among madrepores; here, to protect themselves, they change color, becoming reddish and therefore much harder to spot.

Common genera in the Red Sea:
Caesio.

Lunar Fusilier

Caesio lunaris (Cuvier, 1830)

I   **Fuciliere lunare**
D   **Himmelblauer-Füsilier**
F   **Fusilier lunaire**

28 cm

2-20 m

PERCIFORMES

Caesionidae

Description

The dorsal and ventral profiles of the lunar fusilier are virtually sym
metrical, creating a tapering but robust body shape. Its head i
pointed and its tail is strongly forked.

It is blue, a bit darker dorsally; the tips of the caudal lobes are blac
and a black spot lies at the base of the pectoral fins.

Maximum length 28 cm.

Habitat

It congregates in large schools at outer reef slopes or even at th
inner fringe. It is common at a depth of up to 20 meters.

Distribution

Red Sea and Indo-Pacific region.

Biology and Behavior

A very gregarious species. It feeds on zooplankton and is an indi
cator of the presence of large schools of these organisms.

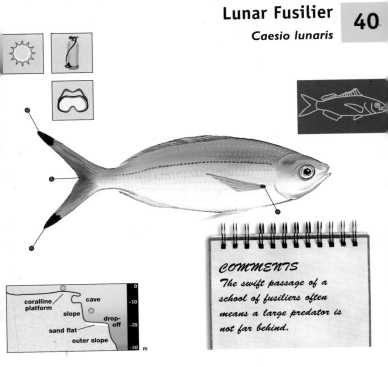

Lunar Fusilier

Caesio lunaris

COMMENTS

The swift passage of a school of fusiliers often means a large predator is not far behind.

coralline platform
cave
slope
drop-off
sand flat
outer slope

0
-10
-20
-30 m

Suez Fusilier

Caesio suevica Klunzinger, 1884

I **Fuciliere di Suez**
D **Rotmeer Füsilier**
F **Fusilier de Suez**

25 cm

2-25 m

Description

A tapering body with symmetrical dorsal and ventral profiles. The head is pointed and the tail strongly forked. The Suez fusilier is silvery blue, with a gold band running around the base of its dorsal fin. The margins of the caudal lobes are black, with a thin white stripe underneath. There is a black spot at the base of the pectoral fins. Maximum length 25 cm.

Habitat

Common on outer reef slopes at a depth of 2-25 meters.

Distribution

Red Sea, Persian Gulf and along the eastern coast of Africa as far as Somalia.

Biology and Behavior

It forms large schools that move in the water opposite the reef slopes. It is a diurnal predator that feeds on zooplankton and takes shelter among the corals at night.

Suez Fusilier

Caesio suevica

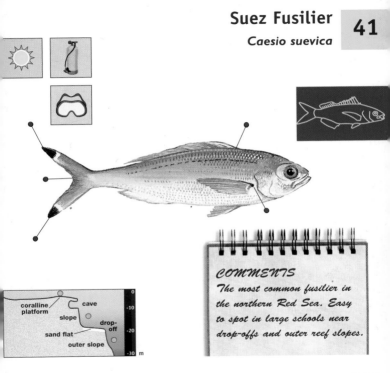

Monotaxis grandoculis (#43)

EMPERORFISHES

These fishes, which the Bedouin call *shaur*, belong to the **Lethrinidae** family, which is typical of the Indo-Pacific region and has many characteristics much like those of the Lutjanidae. There are eleven species of Lethrinidae in the Red Sea, divided into two genera: *Lethrinos* and *Monotaxis*.

They are medium-size fish (30-70 cm) with large scales on their bodies except for the head, a single dorsal fin with bony rays in the anterior portion and soft ones in the posterior portion, and extremely high-set eyes. The emperorfishes' lips are thick, their mouths are in a terminal position, and their teeth are often visible. Some species can rapidly change their color.

These fishes are either solitary or live in schools that sometimes comprise hundreds of individuals, but they are not territorial. Many species of the *Lethrinus* genus are hermaphroditic and protogynous, that is, the females can become males.Emperorfishes are nocturnal predators that live in open waters, but near the outer reef slopes, feeding on invertebrates, crustaceans and fish. They are important economically because they are fished for their tasty meat.

Common genera in the Red Sea:
Lethrinus, Monotaxis.

Spangled Emperor

Lethrinus nebulosus (Forsskål, 1775)

I **Imperatore iridescente**
D **Blauschuppenschnapper**
F **Empereur bleuté**

80 cm

3-75 m

Description

The body of this emperorfish is robust and flattened, high in the anterior portion. The frontal profile is either slanted or slightly convex. Its tail is forked and has pointed margins. Its coloration is bronze, with a yellowish and light blue sheen. Maximum length 80 cm.

Habitat

It frequents protected coral areas or the reef slope up to a depth of 75 meters. It can be seen on algae carpets and even in mangrove swamps.

Distribution

Red Sea and Indo-Pacific region.

Biology and Behavior

While the adults are solitary or somewhat gregarious, the juveniles live in large schools in the most sheltered parts of the reef. Their diet is based on various invertebrates but also includes fish. A longevous species that can live for over 20 years.

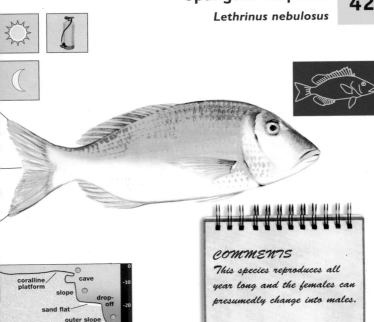

COMMENTS
This species reproduces all year long and the females can presumedly change into males.

coralline platform
cave
slope
drop-off
sand flat
outer slope

0
-10
-20
-30 m

Bigeye Emperor

Monotaxis grandoculis (Forsskål, 1775)

I **Imperatore occhio grosso**
D **Großaugenschnapper**
F **Empereur gros yeux**

60 cm

1-100 m

PERCIFORMES

Lenthrinidae

Description

An oval body with a rather square frontal profile. The tail is strongly forked, the posterior margins of the dorsal and anal fins long and rounded, and the eyes are large. The bigeye emperor is silvery, with a green sheen dorsally. It can change coloration rapidly, four dark vertical bands appearing on its sides. Maximum length 60 cm.

Habitat

It lives in sandy or detrital zones up to a depth of 100 meters.

Distribution

Red Sea and Indo-Pacific region.

Biology and Behavior

The juveniles tend to be solitary, while the adults often form schools of about 50 members. This emperorfish is a nocturnal predator that feeds on a wide range of invertebrates.

Bigeye Emperor

Monotaxis grandoculis

43

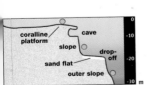

COMMENTS

A genus with one species. Its name derives from its strongly developed eyes.

coralline platform
cave
slope
drop-off
sand flat
outer slope

0
-10
-20
-30 m

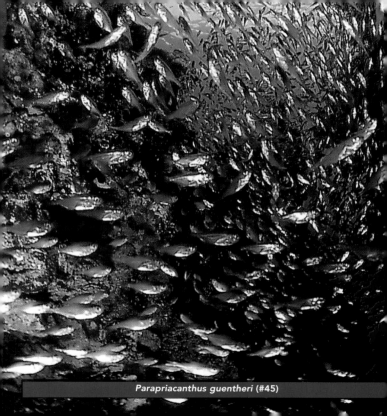

Parapriacanthus guentheri (#45)

SWEEPERS GLASSFISHES

Sweepers and glassfishes are the most characteristic and common dwellers of reef caves and crevices. They belong to the **Pempheridae** family and are distinguished by their small size, translucid ovoid bodies, single dorsal fin and slightly forked tail. Large eyes are a common characteristic among all the Pempherids, which are nocturnal, and their mouths are tiny and slanting. Some species have luminescent organs that are activated during digestion. Sweepers and glassfishes spend the day in large groups so that predators will not be attracted by a single fish; when an intruder arrives, be it a predator or a diver, they quickly scatter all over the cave they are resting in and then form their compact group again once the danger has passed. If approached slowly, they are not difficult to observe and photograph.

At night these fishes move about in search of zooplankton. Sometimes schools of sedentary sweepers and glassfishes can also be seen during the day hovering at the openings of small holes in the reef pinnacles.

Common genera in the Red Sea:
Pempheris, Parapriachantus.

Cave Sweeper (Hatchetfish)

Pempheris vanicolensis Cuvier, 1831

I **Pesce di vetro di grotta**
D **Höhlen-Beilbauchfisch**
F **Hachette des grottes**

18 cm

3-40 m

PERCIFORMES

Pempheridae

Description

A compressed body that is tall in the anterior portion and taperin somewhat toward the tail, which is forked. The coloration is bronze with a black spot marking the apex of the dorsal fin and a blac stripe at the base of the anal fin. Maximum length 18 cm.

Habitat

The cave sweeper is common in the caves of sheltered or expose coralline bottoms at a depth of up to 40 meters.

Distribution

Widespread in the Red Sea and the entire Indo-Pacific region, it ha also lived in the Mediterranean since the opening of the Suez Cana

Biology and Behavior

This species forms dense schools in caves, rubble, and under broa madrepore ledges. At night it moves about in search of zooplanktc and invertebrates.

Cave Sweeper (Hatchetfish)

Pempheris vanicolensis

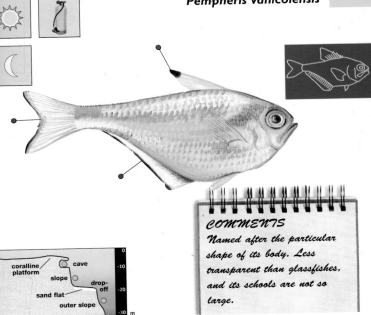

44

COMMENTS
Named after the particular shape of its body. Less transparent than glassfishes, and its schools are not so large.

coralline platform
cave
slope
drop-off
sand flat
outer slope
0
-10
-20
-30 m

45 Glassfish (Red Sea Dwarf Sweeper)

Parapriacanthus guentheri (Steindachner, 1870)

I **Pesce di vetro dorato**
D **Glasfisch**
F **Poisson-hachette nain**

10 cm

2-40 m

Description

A small fish with an oval, tapering body (maximum length 10 cm).
It has only one dorsal fin. The caudal fin is slightly forked. Large eyes.
The head and anterior portion of the sides are gold-colored, while
the rest of the body is transparent and pink.

Habitat

It lives in caves at a depth of up to 40 meters.

Distribution

Red Sea and Indo-Pacific region.

Biology and Behavior

The glassfish is a nocturnal species that spends the day in dense
schools inside grottoes or debris. It can be seen at the base of large
gorgonian branches and moves about at sunset in search of
zooplankton.

Pempheridae

Glassfish (Red Sea Dwarf Sweeper)

Parapriacanthus guentheri

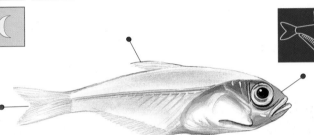

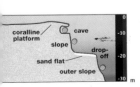

coralline platform
cave
slope
drop-off
sand flat
outer slope

0
-10
-20
-30 m

COMMENTS
A luminescent organ lies in the ventral portion of the body.

Parupeneus cyclostomus (#47)

GOATFISHES

Goatfishes, which belong to the **Mullidae** family, are medium-sized (some species have a maximum length of 60 cm) and have an elongate body covered with large scales, two dorsal fins and a forked tail. They are widespread in all tropical and subtropical seas. In the Red Sea they are represented mainly by seven species belonging to two genera, *Parupeneus* and *Mulloidichthys* (*Mulloides*), characterized by two long barbels beneath the chin at the sides of the mouth which, while the fishes are swimming, look like two slits on its sides. These are special sensory organs with a host of sensitive tips used to find and flush out their prey (mollusks, worms, crustaceans) hidden in the sand. Their small mouths are in a ventral position and have tiny, conical teeth. Goatfishes live in small schools on sandy, shallow sea bottoms and in sheltered areas. When looking for food they stir up clouds of sand in which there are particles of food that attract other fishes—an instance of commensalism. Often a series of small craters on the sandy bottom reveals the passage of goatfishes. Depending on the species, goatfishes are diurnal or nocturnal.

Common genera in the Red Sea:
Mulloidichthys, Parupeneus.

Yellowfin Goatfish

Mulloidichthys vanicolensis (Valenciennes, 1831)

I `    ` **Triglia a pinna gialla**
D `    ` **Großschulenbarbe**
F `    ` **Rouget à nageoires jaunes**

38 cm

5-113 m

PERCIFORMES

Mullidae

Description

A streamlined body with an inclined forehead and mouth with bar
bels. It has two triangular dorsal fins and a strongly forked tail. Th
coloration is pinkish-white with a yellow stripe on the sides from th
eye to the tail. Unpaired yellow fins. Maximum length 38 cm.

Habitat

It lives on coralline or sandy sea floors at a depth of 5-113 meter
in bays sheltered from currents.

Distribution

Widespread in the Red Sea and in the Indo-Pacific region as far a
Japan and Hawaii.

Biology and Behavior

A gregarious species that is inactive by day and at night moves abou
sandy bottoms in search of food.

It preys on common small worms and crustaceans which it finds i
the sandy bottom with its barbels.

Yellowfin Goatfish

Mulloidichthys vanicolensis

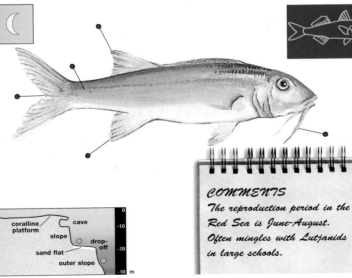

COMMENTS

The reproduction period in the Red Sea is June-August. Often mingles with Lutjanids in large schools.

coralline platform

cave

slope

drop-off

sand flat

outer slope

0
-10
-20
-30 m

Yellowsaddle Goatfish

Parupeneus cyclostomus (Lacepède, 1801)

I **Triglia coda gialla**
D **Gelbsattelbarbe**
F **Rouget doré**

50 cm

3-92 m

Description

A streamlined body with a concave head profile and long barbels, triangular dorsal fins and a strongly forked caudal fin. The body is generally yellow with a blue (or pinkish) sheen on the back, and with a yellow spot on the back of the caudal peduncle. There is a golden yellow variant. Maximum length 50 cm.

Habitat

This goatfish frequents all areas of the reef and the coralline or detrital bottoms at a depth of 3-92 meters.

Distribution

Red Sea and Indo-Pacific region as far as Micronesia.

Biology and Behavior

The juveniles are gregarious, while the adults are more often solitary. It feeds mostly on fish and invertebrates, which it flushes out of the sand with its long barbels. It is diurnal.

PERCIFORMES

Mullidae

Yellowsaddle Goatfish

Parupeneus cyclostomus

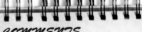

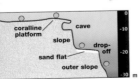

var.

coralline platform

cave

slope

drop-off

sand flat

outer slope

0

-10

-20

-30 m

COMMENTS

Sometimes, when searching for food, it is accompanied by the bluefin trevally and by labrids, which often seize its prey.

PERCIFORMES

Mullidae

Forsskål's Goatfish

Parupeneus forsskali (Fourmanoir & Guézé, 1976)

- I **Triglia di Forsskål**
- D **Forsskals Barbe**
- F **Rouget de Mer Rouge**

28 cm

3-40 m

Description

A streamlined body with the dorsal profile of the head inclined. The mouth has two barbels and opens downwards. The tail is strongly forked. Its coloration is whitish, yellow on the caudal peduncle, which has a black spot. A black band bordered with yellow runs along the sides from the mouth, over the eyes, to the base of the second dorsal fin. Maximum length 28 cm.

Habitat

Sandy bottoms with coralline formations up to 40 meters' depth.

Distribution

Endemic to the Red Sea, it has also lived in the Mediterranean since the construction of the Suez Canal.

Biology and Behavior

This goatfish forms mixed groups consisting of various species of Labridae. It feeds on small invertebrates, which it finds and flushes out of the sandy bottom with its barbels.

Forsskål's Goatfish

Parupeneus forsskali

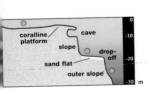

coralline platform

cave

slope

drop-off

sand flat

outer slope

0
-10
-20
-30 m

COMMENTS
The males court the females by touching them with their barbels.

Pomacanthus maculosus (#49)

ANGELFISHES

Angelfishes belong to the **Pomacanthidae** family (from the Greek *poma*, or "cover," and *acanthos*, spine) and are closely related to the butterflyfish family, the Chaetodontidae. They differ from the latter for the large spine on the operculum, the bony plate that protects the gills, and it was only in 1978 that the two families were separated. Pomacanthidae are small or medium-sized fishes (7-70 cm) characterized by their extremely compressed bodies, small and prominent mouth, and very bright colors. There are seven genera in this family and about 80 species. Angelfishes are hermaphroditic and protogynous (they are initially females that become males).

The coloration of the juveniles is strikingly different from that of the adults. Angelfishes are strongly territorial: every male defends its territory (up to 1,000 square meters), in which its harem of 2-5 females lives. Mating normally takes place at sunset: the larvae are pelagic, that is, they live in the open sea, and the larval stage lasts three or four weeks. If disturbed or afraid, angelfishes emit low-frequency sounds that can be heard perfectly by divers.

Common genera in the Red Sea:
Pomacanthus, Pygoplites, Genicanthus, Centropyge, Apolemichthys.

Arabian Angelfish

Pomacanthus maculosus (Forsskål, 1775)

- I **Pesce angelo maculato**
- D **Arabischer Kaiserfisch**
- F **Ange géographe**

 50 cm

 4-50 m

PERCIFORMES

Pomacanthidae

Description

This angelfish has an oval, compressed body that looks square because of the extension of the dorsal and anal fins, the margins of which are very long and threadlike. A pointed head and small, elongate mouth. The coloration is blue, with a vertical yellow spot on its sides. Maximum length 50 cm. Related species: *Pomachantus asfur*.

Habitat

It lives along the reef slopes or on sandy bottoms at a depth of up to 50 meters.

Distribution

Red Sea, Persian Gulf and Gulf of Oman.

Biology and Behavior

A solitary species seen in couples only in the mating season. It feeds on algae, sea squirts and, above all, sponges. The juveniles are blue, with white vertical stripes and take on the adult coloration when they are 10-15 cm long.

Arabian Angelfish

Pomacanthus maculosus

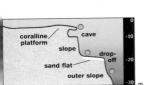

coralline platform

cave

slope

drop-off

sand flat

outer slope

0
-10
-20
-30 m

COMMENTS

This diurnal angelfish spends the night in reef crevices. The yellow spots on its sides are sometimes triangular, resembling the Sinai peninsula.

Emperor Angelfish

Pomacanthus imperator (Bloch, 1787)

I   **Pesce angelo imperatore**
D   **Imperatorkaiserfisch**
F   **Ange empereur**

40 cm

3-70 m

PERCIFORMES

Pomacanthidae

Description

A compressed, square body with a rather pointed head and upward-facing mouth. The margins of the dorsal, anal and caudal fins are rounded. This angelfish is blue, with thin horizontal yellow streaks. The snout is light blue, the tail is yellow, a black mask with a blue border covers the eyes, and a black spot is on the operculum.

Habitat

Zones abounding in corals along the outer reef slope up to a depth of 70 meters.

Distribution

Red Sea and Indo-Pacific region.

Biology and Behavior

A solitary, territorial species that forms couples during the mating season. The adults feed on sponges and other invertebrates, while the juveniles, which live in lagoons and areas with crevices, may behave like cleanerfishes.

Emperor Angelfish
Pomacanthus imperator

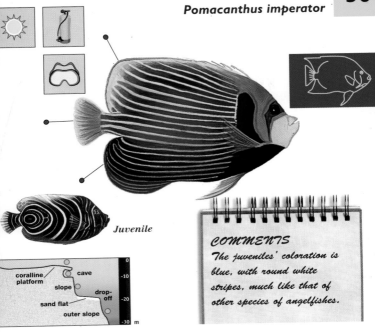

Juvenile

coralline platform
cave
slope
drop-off
sand flat
outer slope

0
-10
-20
-30 m

COMMENTS

The juveniles' coloration is blue, with round white stripes, much like that of other species of angelfishes.

Royal Angelfish

Pygoplites diacanthus (Boddaert, 1772)

- I **Pesce angelo reale**
- D **Pfauenkaiserfisch**
- F **Ange royal**

25 cm

1-48 m

PERCIFORMES

Pomacanthidae

Description

An oval, compressed body with a small, pointed mouth. The margin of the dorsal, anal and caudal fins are rounded. This angelfish i orange, with light blue vertical bands bordered in black. The dorsa fin is blue and the caudal fin is yellow. Maximum length 25 cm.

Habitat

It lives on the outer reefs slopes up to a depth of 48 meters. It als frequents lagoon zones.

Distribution

Red Sea and entire Indo-Pacific region.

Biology and Behavior

The royal angelfish likes areas rich in corals, where it takes refuge i threatened. It can be seen alone or in couples. The juveniles ar orange, and the vertical bands appear as they mature. The diet con sists of sponges, sea squirts and algae.

Royal Angelfish

Pygoplites diacanthus

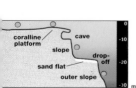

coralline platform
cave
slope
drop-off
sand flat
outer slope

0
-10
-20
-30 m

COMMENTS
The intermediate forms between juveniles and adults have a striking dark ocellus on the dorsal fin.

Chaetodon semilarvatus (#57)

BUTTERFLYFISHES

Chaetodontidae (from the ancient Greek *keta*, silk, and *odontos*, tooth) or butterflyfishes look much like emperorfishes (Pomachantidae) and the two families are the most beautiful and characteristic fish in the Red Sea reefs. There are eleven genera of Chaetodontidae and 116 species, 114 of which belong to the *Chaetodon* genus. Their length ranges from 6 to 30 centimeters and they have a flat, disk-shaped body with a small, protractile mouth with small, densely packed teeth. They often live in couples and the males tend to be monogamous, forming stable relationships that may last for their entire life. Butterflyfishes have a very varied diet; they like algae, fish eggs, and tiny invertebrates, and some species even eat small coral polyps. These latter species are generally more territorial and form large schools with as many as one hundred members. The eggs are pelagic and the larval stage may last for two months; the cranium and anterior portion of the body of the larvae are covered with bony plates.

A feature of the Red Sea butterflyfishes is their high endemicity rate; seven species are known only in this area.

Common genera in the Red Sea:
Chaetodon, Heniochus.

Threadfin Butterflyfish

Chaetodon auriga (Forsskål, 1775)

I   **Pesce farfalla filamentoso**
D   **Fähnchenfalterfisch**
F   **Papillon cocher**

23 cm

1-35 m

PERCIFORMES

Description

A tall, compressed body with a pointed head profile, small, terminal mouth and truncate tail. The dorsal fin has a long posterior filament. The coloration of this butterflyfish is whitish with black diagonal stripes that become attenuated ventrally. A black mask covers the eyes. The unpaired fins are yellow. Maximum length 23 cm.

Habitat

It lives in sandy, detrital or coralline bottoms on the outer slope of the reef at a depth of up to 35 meters.

Distribution

Red Sea and the Indo-Pacific region as far as Micronesia and Japan.

Biology and Behavior

It has varied habits: it can live alone, in couples, or in small groups. It feeds on annelid worms, anemones, coral polyps, crustaceans and algae.

Chaetodontidae

Chaetodon auriga

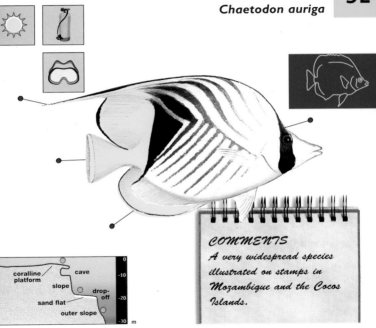

COMMENTS
A very widespread species illustrated on stamps in Mozambique and the Cocos Islands.

coralline platform
cave
0
-10
slope
drop-off
-20
sand flat
outer slope
-30 m

Striped Butterflyfish

Chaetodon fasciatus (Forsskål, 1775)

I **Pesce farfalla fasciato**
D **Tabak-Falterfisch**
F **Papillon tabac**

22 cm

2-25 m

Description

A compressed body made oval by the dorsal and anal fins extending to the tail, which is rounded. Elongate mouth and concave frontal profile. This butterflyfish is yellow, with eleven diagonal black stripes a black dorsal spot and a white frontal one. A black mask covers the eyes. Maximum length 22 cm.

Habitat

It lives in shallow habitats rich in corals at depths of up to 25 meters

Distribution

An endemic Red Sea species also seen in the Gulf of Aden.

Biology and Behavior

It lives in couples or in small groups in areas rich in corals, which i feeds on. Its diet also includes algae and various invertebrates. It ma occasionally form larger schools. The juveniles have a posterio ocellum.

COMMENTS
The black diagonal bands
are unmistakable. One of the
most common butterflyfishes,
rarely leading a solitary life.

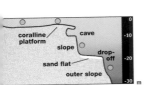

coralline platform
cave
slope
drop-off
sand flat
outer slope
0
-10
-20
-30 m

E

Orangehead Butterflyfish

Chaetodon larvatus Cuvier, 1831

I **Pesce farfalla dal muso arancione**
D **Orangekopf-Falterfisch**
F **Papillon à tête orange**

12 cm

3-12 m

Description

A tall, compressed body with a square profile. The mouth is small and pointed, the caudal fin truncate or slightly rounded. This fish is light blue with vertical yellow stripes on its sides and a black spot covering part of the dorsal and caudal fins. The head is reddish. Maximum length 12 cm.

Habitat

It inhabits areas rich in corals up to a depth of 12 meters.

Distribution

An endemic Red Sea and Gulf of Aden species.

Biology and Behavior

It marks out territories on the bottom rich in madrepores of the Acropora genus, where it moves about in couples. It feeds mainly on coral polyps. It is diurnal.

Orangehead Butterflyfish

Chaetodon larvatus

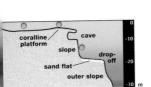

coralline platform

cave

slope

drop-off

sand flat

outer slope

0
-10
-20
-30 m

COMMENTS
Like many other butterfly-fishes, this one seizes coral polyps with its pointed mouth.

Lined Butterflyfish

Chaetodon lineolatus Cuvier, 1831

I **Pesce farfalla striato**
D **Riesenfalterfisch**
F **Papillon linéolé**

30 cm

2-171 m

PERCIFORMES

Chaetodontidae

Description

A tall, compressed body with a long pointed mouth. The caudal fin is rounded, as are the margins of the dorsal and anal fins. The coloration is white on the sides, with vertical black stripes. A black band covers the eyes and another one goes from the base of the dorsal fin to the caudal peduncle. The fins are yellow.

Maximum length 30 cm.

Habitat

It inhabits coralline bottoms up to a depth of 171 meters.

Distribution

Red Sea and Indo-Pacific region as far as Japan and Micronesia.

Biology and Behavior

A territorial species that is aggressive with other fish and is solitary or lives in couples on bottoms with much coral vegetation. It feeds on coral polyps, anemones, small invertebrates and algae, which it seizes and pulls off with its long, thin mouth.

Lined Butterflyfish

Chaetodon lineolatus

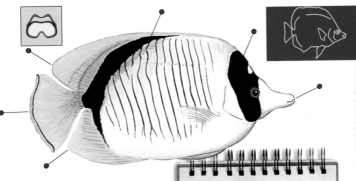

COMMENTS

This is the largest butterfly fish of this genus. It is rather rare and timid.

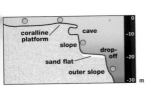

Crown Butterflyfish

Chaetodon paucifasciatus (Ahl, 1923)

I **Pesce farfalla coronato**
D **Rotfleck-Falterfisch**
F **Papillon orange**

14 cm

4-30 m

Description

A tall and compressed body profile with a pointed head and mouth
The margins of the dorsal, anal and caudal fins are rounded. The sides
are yellowish, with black diagonal stripes. The posterior portion of
the body is white, with a reddish vertical band that covers the dorsal
fin and caudal peduncle. The tail is red-bordered.
Maximum length 14 cm.

Habitat

It inhabits sea floors with rubble or corals up to 30 meters' depth.

Distribution

An endemic species of the Red Sea and Gulf of Aden.

Biology and Behavior

It lives in couples or small groups that move among corals in search
of food, which basically consists of coral polyps as well as algae,
annelid worms and small crustaceans. The juveniles have a black posterior ocellum.

COMMENTS

Very popular in tropical marine aquariums, so it is important commercially. Rather rare in the northern Red Sea.

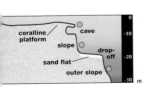

coralline platform
cave
slope
drop-off
sand flat
outer slope

0
-10
-20
-30 m

Masked Butterflyfish

Chaetodon semilarvatus Cuvier, 1831

I   **Pesce farfalla mascherato**
D   **Maskenfalterfisch**
F   **Papillon jaune**

23 cm

3-20 m

Description

An almost disk-shaped body that is compressed, with a pointed head and the mouth in a terminal position. The margins of the unpaired fins are rounded. Coloration yellow, with thirteen darker vertical bands on the sides, and a broad bluish spot from the eyes to the throat. Maximum length 23 cm.

Habitat

It lives in areas rich in coral growth and sandy bottoms, up to depth of 20 meters.

Distribution

An endemic Red Sea and Gulf of Aden species.

Biology and Behavior

This butterflyfish is quite common in the Red Sea, often seen in couples in areas rich in madrepores. It may also form small groups. It is active at sunset or at night and feeds on coral polyps, soft corals and small invertebrates.

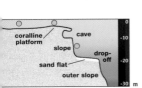

coralline platform
cave
slope
drop-off
sand flat
outer slope

0
-10
-20
-30 m

COMMENTS
A very common species. During the day it rests for long periods under broad madrepore ledges.

Red Sea Bannerfish

Heniochus intermedius (Steindachner, 1893)

I **Pesce farfalla bandiera**
D **Rotmeer-Wimpelfisch**
F **Poisson-cocher commun**

20 cm

3-50 m

Description

A square, compressed body characterized by the long ray on the dorsal fin after which this species is named. The mouth is long and the caudal fin rounded or truncate. The body is white dorsally and yellow ventrally, while the sides have two wide black diagonal bands. Maximum length 20 cm. Related species: *H. diphreutes*.

Habitat

It frequents sheltered or exposed coralline bottoms up to a depth of 50 meters.

Distribution

A species endemic to the Red Sea and Gulf of Aden.

Biology and Behavior

The juveniles are gregarious, while the adults are territorial and live in stable couples. It feeds on a vast range of planktonic and benthic invertebrates. It swims by moving its caudal fin but is quite agile among the corals by using its pectoral fins.

Red Sea Bannerfish 58

Heniochus intermedius

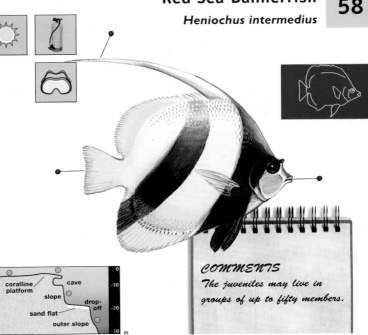

COMMENTS

The juveniles may live in groups of up to fifty members.

coralline platform
cave
slope
drop-off
sand flat
outer slope

0
-10
-20
-30 m

Oxycirrhites typus (#59)

HAWKFISHES

Hawkfishes belong to the small **Cirrhitidae** family, which has nine genera with 35 species and lives above all in the Indo-Pacific region. In the Red Sea this family is represented by four genera and four species.

Hawkfishes are small (10-20 centimeters) and their characteristic feature consists of the tiny tufts of filaments, called *cirrhi* in Latin, at the end of the spinous rays on the single dorsal fin. The rather robust pectoral fins have 14 thick, long rays.

During the day hawkfishes hover among the madrepores in the reef, preferably on gorgonians: thanks to their strong pectoral fins, they are able to climb and "stand" among the coral growth, where they remain motionless even for hours, lying in ambush for their prey, usually small fish or crustaceans. This special hunting technique, similar to that of birds of prey, has earned them their name.

When their prey swims past, the hawkfishes snap it up with a sudden, swift lunge. These fishes are territorial and normally a male has a harem. The eggs are laid in the open sea, where they float together with plankton.

Common genera in the Red Sea:
Oxycirrhites, Paracirrhites.

Longnose Hawkfish

Oxycirrhites typus (Bleeker, 1857)

I   **Pesce falco a scacchi rossi**
D   **Langnasenbüschelbarsch**
F   **Poisson-faucon à long nez**

13 cm

10-100 m

PERCIFORMES

Description

A tapering body with a long mouth facing slightly upward. The dorsal fin is supported by spinous rays, the caudal fin is weakly forked. The coloration of this hawkfish is typical, consisting of a series of horizontal and vertical red stripes against a white ground. Maximum length 13 cm.

Habitat

This species lives in shallow waters rich in corals and on the seaward slope of the reef at a depth of up to 100 meters.

Distribution

Red Sea and the Indo-Pacific region as far as the West Coast of the United States.

Biology and Behavior

It lives among gorgonian branches, where it is camouflaged and lies in wait for its prey (small crustaceans). This is a hermaphroditic species whose females can become males. It lives in harems.

Cirrhitidae

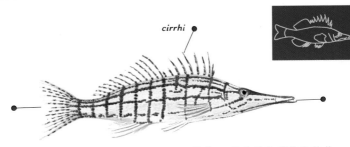

cirrhi

COMMENTS

Its checkered coloration is perfect camouflage among the branches of acropora. It lays its eggs on the sea bottom.

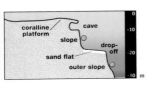

coralline platform

cave

slope

drop-off

sand flat

outer slope

0

-10

-20

-30 m

Forster's Hawkfish

Paracirrhites forsteri (Schneider, 1801)

I **Pesce falco di Forster**
D **Forsters Büschelbarsch**
F **Poisson-faucon de Forster**

 22 cm

 1-40 m

PERCIFORMES

Cirrhitidae

Description

A tapering body that is tall in the anterior portion. The dorsal fin is supported by spinous rays, the caudal fin is slightly rounded and often closes like a fan. Brownish-yellow coloration, with a broad, dark dorsal band. The head is dotted with reddish spots. The color changes with age and among different individuals. Maximum length 22 cm.

Habitat

It lives on coralline bottoms up to a depth of 40 meters.

Distribution

Red Sea and the entire Indo-Pacific region.

Biology and Behavior

It hovers on large madrepore formations waiting for fish to pass by. Besides fish, it also feeds on small crustaceans. This is a territorial species that lives in harems with one dominating male.

Forster's Hawkfish

Paracirrhites forsteri

cirrhi

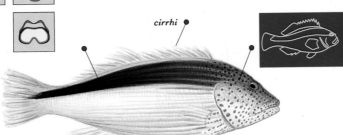

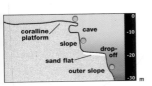

coralline platform
cave
slope
drop-off
sand flat
outer slope

0
-10
-20
-30 m

COMMENTS

Common on Acropora and
Pocillopora madrepores and
fire corals (Millepora).
Illustrated on the stamps
of the Cocos Islands.

Amphiprion bicinctus (#68)

DAMSELFISHES – PULLERS
ANEMONEFISHES
SERGEANTFISHES

Damselfishes, pullers (or chromis), sergeantfishes and anemonefishes all belong to the **Pomacentridae** family, which comprises over 300 species distributed in all tropical and subtropical seas. The Pomacentridae are represented in the Red Sea by 12 genera and 35 species, ten of which are endemic.

Common features of all the members of this family are their small size (2-20 centimeters), their tall, compressed bodies covered with medium-sized to large scales, a continuous dorsal fin with rigid rays in the anterior portions and soft ones in the posterior portion, and a small, terminal mouth. Some juvenile species have different coloration from that of the adults. Pomacentridae are typical reef fishes, whose feeding habits vary according to the genus (they feed either on algae or plankton or are ominivorous). Anemonefishes live in symbiosis with anemones. In general, Pomacentridae are diurnal, they tend to live in groups, are territorial and aggressive. When in danger, they hide inside madrepores, preferably acropores.

Common genera in the Red Sea:
Pomacentrus, Dascyllus, Chromis, Amphiprion, Adudefduf.

Sulphur Damselfish

Pomacentrus sulfureus (Klunzinger, 1871)

I **Damigella sulfurea**
D **Zitronengelbe Demoiselle**
F **Demoiselle soufrée**

 11 cm

1-10 m

PERCIFORMES

Description
An elongate, oval body with a pointed head. The tail is slightly forked, with rounded lobes. The coloration is yellow, a bit darker dorsally. A black spot lies at the base of the pectoral fin. The juveniles have a black spot on the dorsal fin. Maximum length 11 cm.

Habitat
This damselfish lives in shallow water in areas rich in coral growth, lagoons and sheltered parts of the reef, at a depth of up to 10 meters.

Distribution
Red Sea and west Indian Ocean.

Biology and Behavior
It feeds on different zooplankton and algae. It uses its dorsal fins to move about with agility among the madrepore branches.

Pomacentridae

Sulphur Damselfish

Pomacentrus sulfureus

COMMENTS

A very common and solitary species that frequents acropora, where it finds an abundance of zooplankton and algae.

Whitebelly Damselfish

Amblyglyphidodon leucogaster (Bleeker, 1847)

- I **Damigella a ventre bianco**
- D **Weißbauch-Riffbarsch**
- F **Demoiselle à ventre blanc**

13 cm

2-45 m

PERCIFORMES

Pomacentridae

Description

An oval, compressed body with a small head and terminal mouth
The caudal fin is forked. It is bluish-green, lighter ventrally. The
unpaired fins are bordered in black and the opercular zone i
blackish. Maximum length 13 cm.

Habitat

This damselfish likes sheltered coralline areas or the reef slopes, a
a depth of up to 45 meters.

Distribution

Red Sea and Indo-Pacific region.

Biology and Behavior

It is solitary or lives in small groups. It feeds mainly on zooplankton
and sometimes algae. The great range of its coloration in differen
regions has led some zoologists to believe that several species ar
classified with the same name.

Whitebelly Damselfish

Amblyglyphidodon leucogaster

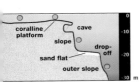

coralline platform · cave · slope · drop-off · sand flat · outer slope

0 · -10 · -20 · -30 m

COMMENTS

This genus is represented in the Red Sea by only one other species, A. flavilatus, which has yellow sides.

Banded Dascyllus

Dascyllus aruanus (Linnaeus, 1758)

- **I** **Damigella fasciata**
- **D** **Dreibinden-Preußenfisch**
- **F** **Demoiselle-bonbon**

8 cm

1-20 m

PERCIFORMES

Pomacentridae

Description

An oval body with a rather high dorsal fin and terminal mouth. The caudal fin is forked, with rounded lobes. The body is white, with three vertical black stripes going from the dorsal fin to the anal fin, ventral fins and the mouth. Maximum length 8 cm.

Habitat

It frequents protected areas rich in corals, at a depth of up to 2? meters.

Distribution

Quite widespread in the Red Sea and Indo-Pacific region.

Biology and Behavior

The banded dascyllus lives in schools among the ramifications of *St lophora, Pocillopora* and *Acropora* corals. It is a territorial species tha feeds on zooplankton, various invertebrates and algae.

The males prepare the nest and invite the females to lay their egg which hatch in five days.

Banded Dascyllus

Dascyllus aruanus

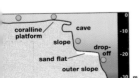

COMMENTS
The males watch over the
eggs and defend them
vigorously against intruders.

Domino

Dascyllus trimaculatus (Rüppell, 1829)

I **Damigella domino**
D **Dreifleck-Preußenfisch**
F **Demoiselle domino**

14 cm

1-55 m

PERCIFORMES

Pomacentridae

Description

An oval, compressed body with a slightly inclined head profile. The tail is slightly forked and has rounded margins. The domino is dark with a white spot on either side at the base of the dorsal fin. The juveniles also have a white frontal spot, hence the name *trimaculatus* or "three-spotted." Maximum length 14 cm.

Habitat

It lives in zones rich in corals, either sheltered or on the seaward reef slope, up to a depth of 55 meters. It often mingles with anemones.

Distribution

Quite widespread in the Red Sea and Indo-Pacific region.

Biology and Behaviors

A gregarious species that lives in harems dominated by one male. The eggs are laid on the rocky slope or among corals and are watched over by the males until they hatch. It feeds on algae and planktonic crustaceans.

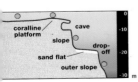

COMMENTS

The juveniles live in large groups, sometimes mingling with large anemones.

Half-and-Half Chromis

Chromis dimidiata (Klunzinger, 1871)

I **Castagnola bianca e nera**
D **Zweifarb-Schwalbenschwanz**
F **Castagnole bicolore**

 9 cm

 1-36 m

PERCIFORMES

Pomacentridae

Description

An oval, compressed body with a small terminal mouth. The tail strongly forked. This species is easy to recognize for its characteristic color: the anterior portion is brown and the posterior half white. Maximum length 9 cm.

Habitat

It lives in lagoons with an abundance of madrepores or on the seaward reef slope, up to a depth of 36 meters. It often mingles with fire corals (genus *Millepora*).

Distribution

Red Sea and Indian Ocean.

Biology and Behavior

This chromis forms small schools near the bottom or in broad madrepore ledges.

During the reproduction period it becomes strongly territorial. feeds mainly on zooplankton, but also likes algae.

Half-and-Half Chromis

Chromis dimidiata

COMMENTS

Extremely widespread among acropore branches, where it hides when threatened. Often together with Chromis viridis.

Bluegreen Puller (Chromis)

Chromis viridis (Cuvier, 1830)

I **Castagnola verde-blu**
D **Grüner Riffbarsch**
F **Castagnole verte**

7 cm

1-12 m

PERCIFORMES

Pomacentridae

Description
The body is oval and regular, with a clearly forked tail. Its coloration
is blue-green, lighter ventrally. During the reproduction period the
males' dorsal fin becomes black and yellow. Maximum length 7 cm.

Habitat
This puller likes sheltered lagoon areas rich in corals, from the surface to a depth of 12 meters.

Distribution
It lives in the tropical and subtropical areas of the Red Sea and
throughout the Indo-Pacific region.

Biology and Behavior
A strongly gregarious species that prefers to group together among
the branches of acropores, where the juveniles tend to remain in
hiding. The males prepare the nests and invite several females there.
The diet consists of algae and planktonic invertebrates.

Bluegreen Puller (Chromis)

Chromis viridis

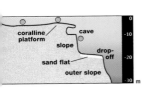

coralline platform
cave
slope
drop-off
sand flat
outer slope

COMMENTS
It lives in large schools.
After fecundating the eggs,
the males oxygenate them by
moving the water with their
fins until they hatch.

Red Sea Anemonefish

Amphiprion bicinctus (Rüppell, 1830)

I **Pesce pagliaccio bifasciato**
D **Rotmeer-Anemonenfisch**
F **Poisson-clown à deux bandes**

12 cm

1-30 m

PERCIFORMES

Pomacentridae

Description

An oval, regularly shaped body with rounded pectoral fins and a slightly forked caudal fin. It is orange, darker dorsally. Two bluish-white vertical spots with black edges are on the head and sides. Maximum length 12 cm.

Habitat

It lives in symbiosis with anemones at a depth of up to 30 meters.

Distribution

From the Red Sea to the Chagos Islands.

Biology and Behavior

This is a territorial, aggressive species that lives in couples among the urticating tentacles of anemones to hide from predators.

When the female (which is larger) dies, the male changes sex.

The eggs are laid at the base of the anemone and the male watches over them. These fish feed on algae, invertebrates and "leftovers" from its host.

Red Sea Anemonefish

Amphiprion bicinctus

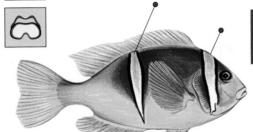

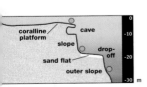

coralline platform
cave
slope
drop-off
sand flat
outer slope
0
-10
-20
-30 m

COMMENTS
It does not hesitate to attack
fish and even divers that come
too close to the anemone with
which it lives in symbiosis.

Sergeant Major

Abudefduf vaigiensis (Quoy & Gaimard, 1825)

I   **Pesce sergente maggiore**
D   **Indopazifischer Soldatenfisch**
F   **Sergent-major**

18 cm

0-15 m

PERCIFORMES

Pomacentridae

Description

A compact, oval, regular body. The caudal fin is clearly forked. The coloration is golden dorsally and silver ventrally and laterally. Five vertical black bands are on the sides of the body. Unlike *A. sexfasciatus*, this species has a uniformly silver tail. The adult males become bluish during the reproduction period. Maximum length 18 cm.

Habitat

Shallow reef water up to a depth of 15 meters.

Distribution

Widespread in the tropical and subtropical seas, it recently penetrated into the Mediterranean as well.

Biology and Behavior

This is a very gregarious and curious species that even approaches humans when looking for food. It feeds on algae, invertebrates and small fish. The juveniles live in dense schools in calm lagoon water.

Sergeant Major

Abudefduf vaigiensis

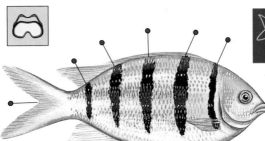

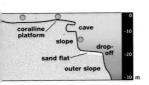

coralline platform
cave
slope
drop-off
sand flat
outer slope

0
-10
-20
-30 m

COMMENTS
The adult males prepare the nest among the corals and take care of the eggs.
Related species: A. vaigiensis.

Scissortail Sergeant

Abudefduf sexfasciatus (Lacepède, 1801)

I **Sergente dalla coda a forbice**
D **Scherenschwanz-Soldatenfisch**
F **Sergent-major à queue en ciseaux**

16 cm

0-15 m

PERCIFORMES

Pomacentridae

Description

The body is oval and regular. The profile of the head is slightly pointed and the tail strongly forked. This species is silvery, with five black vertical bands. The lobes of the caudal fin have black borders. Maximum length 16 cm.

Habitat

It lives on coralline sea floors up to a depth of 15 meters.

Distribution

Quite common in the Red Sea and Indo-Pacific region.

Biology and Behavior

This sergeantfish forms large schools in shallow waters and often in the fringe areas. It feeds on algae and zooplankton.

One of the most common and easily observable fish, even from the surface, since it congregates under boats and piers.

Scissortail Sergeant

Abudefduf sexfasciatus

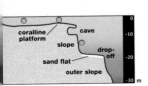

coralline platform
cave
slope
drop-off
sand flat
outer slope

0
-10
-20
-30 m

COMMENTS

Very common in the Gulf of Aqaba. It swims by using its caudal fin to move about rapidly.

Cheilinus undulatus (#72)

CLEANERFISHES
NAPOLEONFISHES
WRASSES

Cleanerfishes, napoleonfishes and wrasses all belong to the large and heterogeneous **Labridae** family, which comprises about 500 species that live in all the seas of the world. There are great differences among them in size (from a few centimeters to more than two meters) and morphology, but they all have a single dorsal fin with bony rays, cycloid scales and fleshy labial folds, hence the name of the family.

Another feature of labrids is that they use their pectoral fins for propulsion and not the caudal fin, which is used as a rudder. Their bright colors change even within the same species according to their sex and age. In general, labrids are carnivorous and rigorously diurnal. They feed on small invertebrates, even though some species like plankton, corals and fish.

Cleanerfishes should be described separately. They feed on ectoparasites that live on the flesh of other fish, thus engaging in a particular form of symbiosis. Each stretch of reef has its "cleaning station" in which fish stop to have the cleanerfishes "disinfect" them.

Common genera in the Red Sea:
Labroides, Bodianus, Cheilinus, Thalassoma, Coris, Epibulus.

Cleaner Wrasse

Labroides dimidiatus (Valenciennes, 1839)

I **Pesce pulitore**
D **Gewöhnlicher Putzerlippfisch**
F **Girelle nettoyeuse commune**

11 cm

1-40 m

PERCIFORMES

Labridae

Description

The body is thin and elongate, with a pointed head and truncate or slightly rounded tail. The coloration is bluish-white, with a striking black stripe that crosses the sides from the mouth to the tail. Dorsally it may have a golden sheen. Maximum length 11 cm.

Habitat

It lives on sheltered coralline sea floors or along the seaward slope of the reef up to a depth of 40 meters.

Distribution

Red Sea and Indo-Pacific region.

Biology and Behavior

This is the most common cleanerfish, whose "job" is to eliminate parasites, food residue and pieces of tissue from the bodies of other fishes, even going into their mouths or gills to do so. It establishes small territories that become its cleaning stations. A recognition ritual precedes the actual cleaning.

Cleaner Wrasse

Labroides dimidiatus

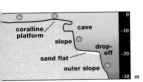

coralline platform — cave — slope — drop-off — sand flat — outer slope

COMMENTS
It can live alone, in couples or in small harems.
There is sexual inversion from female to male.

Bodianus Axillaris

Bodianus axillaris (Bennett, 1832)

I **Labride macchiato**
D **Zweifleck Schweinslippfisch**
F **Poisson-cochon à tache noire**

 20 cm

2-40 m

Description

A tapering body with a slightly elongate mouth and truncate tail. The dorsal fin has spinous rays. The anterior portion of the body is reddish-brown, while the posterior portion is white. The median fins are yellow. A black spot is on the dorsal, anal and pectoral fins.
Maximum length 20 cm.

Habitat

It lives on the coralline bottoms of lagoons or along reef slopes at depth of up to 40 meters.

Distribution

Red Sea and Indo-Pacific region.

Biology and Behavior

The adults are solitary and feed on small fish and invertebrates, especially mollusks and crustaceans. The juveniles, which are black with brilliant round white spots, take shelter in the reef crevices among the corals, behaving like cleanerfishes.

Bodianus Axillaris

Bodianus axillaris

COMMENTS
The adult and juvenile coloration is completely different. This species is illustrated on Cocos Islands stamps.

Napoleonfish

Cheilinus undulatus (Rüppell, 1835)

I **Pesce Napoleone**
D **Napoleon-Lippfisch**
F **Napoléon**

230 cm

1-60 m

Description

This is the largest labrid, whose maximum length can exceed two meters. Its body is tall and compressed, characterized by a frontal protuberance that grows with age. It has a protractile mouth, fleshy lips and a rounded tail. The adults' color is blue-green, sometimes with a purple sheen. The juveniles have a lighter color.

Habitat

It lives in sheltered areas and on the reef slopes up to a depth of 60 meters.

Distribution

Red Sea and Indo-Pacific region as far as Micronesia.

Biology and Behavior

A species that tends to be solitary, sedentary and diurnal, sleeping among the corals at night. It feeds on fish, mollusks and crustaceans and is one of the few predators able to feed on poisonous species. It is not afraid of humans.

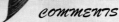

coralline platform
cave
slope
drop-off
sand flat
outer slope

0
-10
-20
-10 m

COMMENTS

An endangered species because of indiscriminate fishing. Its meat, especially the lips, is in great demand.

Klunzinger's Wrasse

Thalassoma rueppellii (Klunzinger, 1871)

I   **Donzella di Klunzinger**
D   **Rotmeer-Junker**
F   **Girelle de Klunzinger**

20 cm

1-20 m

Description

A fish with a tapering body, pointed head and truncate caudal fin with elongate margins. Its basic color is green dorsally and light blue ventrally, with a red stripe along the sides. The head has patterns of the same color. Maximum length 20 cm.

Habitat

This wrasse likes the seaward reef slopes, even in the fringe area. It lives at a depth of up to 20 meters.

Distribution

An endemic Red Sea species, one of the most common and easiest to observe.

Biology and Behavior

It feeds on various invertebrates but can also behave like a cleaner-fish. Some females of this species change sex during their lifetime, so that there are two types of males, primary and secondary.
It is curious and approaches divers without fear.

Klunzinger's Wrasse

Thalassoma rueppellii

NOTE
The old scientific name of this
species, *Thalassoma Klunzingeri*,
is no longer accepted.

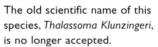

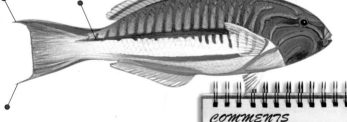

COMMENTS
The primary males couple
in mixed groups, while the
secondary males are
territorial and solitary,
even during courtship.

coralline platform
cave
slope
drop-off
sand flat
outer slope

0
-10
-20
-30 m

Moon Wrasse

Thalassoma lunare (Linnaeus, 1758)

I **Donzella dalla coda falcata**
D **Mondschwanz-Lippfisch**
F **Girelle-lune**

 25 cm

1-20 m

PERCIFORMES

Description

An elongate body with a rounded head and crescent-shaped tail. The pectoral fins are rounded. Its color is blue-green and green posteriorly. The center of the pectoral fins is violet and there are violet stripes on the head.

Habitat

It can be seen in shallow lagoon water and on the exposed side of the reef at a depth of up to 20 meters.

Distribution

Red Sea and along the East African coast. Also widespread in the Indo-Pacific region as far as New Zealand.

Biology and Behavior

It feeds on small invertebrates and fish eggs. The juveniles behave like cleanerfishes. There are primary males and females that change sex becoming secondary males. This wrasse lives in mixed groups in which the males have harems.

Labridae

Moon Wrasse

Thalassoma lunare

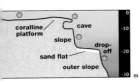

coralline platform
cave
slope
drop-off
sand flat
outer slope

0
-10
-20
-30 m

COMMENTS

One of the most common labrids in the northern Red Sea. The females' color is lighter, tending toward green.

Scarus gibbus (#76)

PARROTFISHES

Parrotfishes belong to the **Scaridae** family, which has about 80 species in the circumtropical regions. Their characteristic feature is the mouth, which has two robust incisor teeth that are joined and create a "beak" that can easily break madrepores and pick up tiny algae off the rocks.

Their body is covered with large scales and has a single dorsal fin; the pectoral fins are well developed and their brilliant coloration varies according to sex and age.

Like the Labridae (see p. 203), female parrotfishes change sex during their lifetime. These fishes also use their pectoral fins for propulsion and feed mostly on algae during the day.

Thanks to their special teeth, parrotfishes can break and crush madrepore corals, which they expel in the form of fine-grained sand. This characteristic of the Scaridae is responsible for the coralline beaches: the annual production of this fine sand by a single parrotfish has been estimated at hundreds of kilograms.

At night these fishes sleep in the reef crevices, wrapped in a "case" of mucus that they secrete to protect themselves from predators.

Common genera in the Red Sea:
Scarus, Cetoscarus, Bolbometopon.

E

Scaridae

Rusty Parrotfish

Scarus ferrugineus Forsskål, 1775

I **Pesce pappagallo rugginoso**
D **Rostpapageienfisch**
F **Perroquet rouillé**

41 cm

1-60 m

Description

An oval body with a regularly shaped head and beak-like jaw. The ta
is rounded in the females and truncate with pointed margins in th
males. The coloration varies according to sex and age. The juvenile
are brown with dark vertical stripes. The males have an orange heac
light blue sides and the posterior portion of the body is greenish
Maximum length 41 cm.

Habitat

It lives in different parts of the reef, in particular on the slopes, up to
a depth of 60 meters; it prefers areas with a lot of shelters.

Distribution

An endemic Red Sea species.

Biology and Behavior

The juveniles are females that change sex and coloration, becoming
secondary males. These latter are territorial and have harems. This
species feeds on algae it finds after pulverizing the corals.

Rusty Parrotfish

Scarus ferrugineus

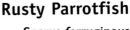

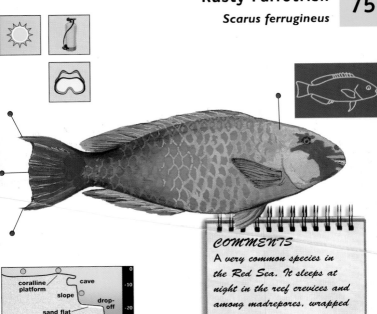

COMMENTS

A very common species in the Red Sea. It sleeps at night in the reef crevices and among madrepores, wrapped in a mucus case.

coralline platform
cave
slope
drop-off
sand flat
outer slope

0
-10
-20
-30 m

Red Sea Steep-Headed Parrotfish

Scarus (Chlorurus) gibbus (Rüppell, 1829)

E

I **Pesce pappagallo camuso**
D **Buckelkopf-Papageienfisch**
F **Perroquet gibbus**

70 cm

1-35 m

PERCIFORMES

Scaridae

Description

This parrotfish has an elongate, robust body with a square-shaped frontal profile in the adult males. Its tail is crescent-shaped, with elongate margins. The beak-shaped teeth are joined. The coloration is blue, with a green and purple sheen in the males, a yellowish one in the females. Maximum length 70 cm. Marked sexual dimorphism that may cause problems in identifying the species.

Habitat

Common on the outer reefs up to a depth of 35 meters.

Distribution

This species is officially recognized only in the Red Sea and is sometimes mistaken for other species in the Indo-Pacific region.

Biology and Behavior

The juveniles are solitary and are characterized by their horizontal white and black stripes. The adults are gregarious. They feed on algae that live on or in corals.

Scarus (Chlorurus) gibbus

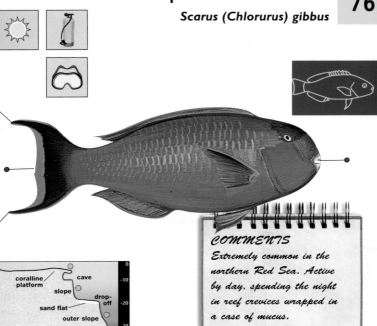

COMMENTS

Extremely common in the northern Red Sea. Active by day, spending the night in reef crevices wrapped in a case of mucus.

coralline platform
cave
slope
drop-off
sand flat
outer slope

0
-10
-20
-30 m

Bullethead Parrotfish

Scarus (Chlorurus) sordidus (Forsskål. 1775)

I **Pesce pappagallo dal muso tondo**
D **Kugelkopf-Papageifisch**
F **Perroquet brûlé**

 40 cm

 1-25 m

PERCIFORMES

Description
An oval, compressed body, with a regularly shaped head with joined teeth that form a beak. The tail is truncate. The color varies quite a lot according to sex and age: at first it is generally brown with a pink head and a few white spots on its sides. The adult males are green with yellow cheeks. Maximum length 40 cm.

Habitat
It can live both in sandy zones and on the outer reef, at a depth of up to 25 meters.

Distribution
This is probably the most common parrotfish in the Red Sea. Widespread in the Indo-Pacific region as far as Hawaii.

Biology and Behavior
There are primary males and females that change sex, becoming secondary males. The juveniles are gregarious and go from the grazing areas to the rest areas.

Scaridae

Bullethead Parrotfish

Scarus (Chlorurus) sordidus

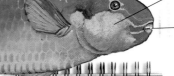

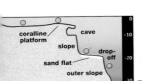

coralline platform

cave

slope

drop-off

sand flat

outer slope

0
-10
-20
-30 m

COMMENTS

This species feeds on the stringy algae on madrepores, which it breaks and grinds, forming clouds of fine coralline sand.

Bicolour Parrotfish

Cetoscarus bicolor (Rüppell, 1829)

I **Pesce pappagallo bicolore**
D **Masken-Papageifisch**
F **Perroquet bicolore**

90 cm

1-30 m

PERCIFORMES

Description

This species has an oval, elongate body and its mouth is like a beak. The tail is crescent-shaped.

The coloration depends on the sex and age. The juveniles are whitish, with brown heads. The adult males are green, but their fins and the border of the scales are violet. The females are brownish-yellow, with dark fins. Marked sexual dimorphism.

Habitat

It lives in lagoons and along the outer reefs up to a depth of 30 meters.

Distribution

Red Sea and Indo-Pacific region.

Scaridae

Biology and Behavior

The juveniles are solitary, while the adult males have harems scattered in vast territories. Reproduction occurs in groups and in areas with currents so the eggs can be transported to the open sea. It feeds on the algae that cover madrepores.

Bicolour Parrotfish

Cetoscarus bicolor

78

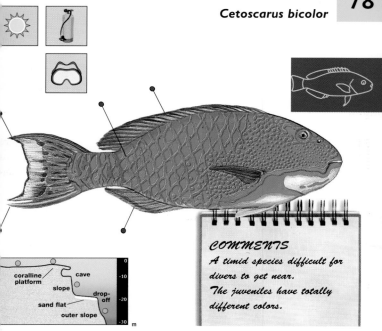

COMMENTS

A timid species difficult for divers to get near.

The juveniles have totally different colors.

coralline platform
cave
slope
drop-off
sand flat
outer slope

0
-10
-20
-30 m

Sphyraena barracuda (#79)

BARRACUDA

Barracuda belong to the **Sphyraenidae** family, which has only one genus, *Sphyraena*, with 18 species, five of which live in the Red Sea: *S. barracuda*, the great barracuda, a large, solitary creature; *S. qenie*, the blackfin barracuda, which is much smaller and has 20 dark bands on its body; *S. flavicauda*, the yellowtail barracuda; *S. jello* and *S. putnamiae*.

Barracuda live in all tropical and subtropical seas and are considered among the most voracious and ferocious predators. However, they are not particularly dangerous for human beings. These fish prefer the open waters near the reef and are active during the day. The juveniles tend to form large groups with hundreds or even thousands of members that often swim together in a vortex-like formation, as can be seen in the Ras Mohammed National Park area, especially in July and August.

CIGUATERA

Barracuda are often fished for their tasty meat, but in certain regions (especially in the Atlantic and Pacific) they may cause *Ciguatera*, a serious form of intoxication caused by a seaweed eaten by reef fishes that are in turn the barracuda's prey.

Common genera in the Red Sea:
Sphyraena.

Great Barracuda

Sphyraena barracuda (Walbaum, 1792)

I   **Grande barracuda**
D   **Großer Barrakuda**
F   **Grand barracuda**

200 cm

0-100 m

PERCIFORMES

Sphyraenidae

Description

An elongate, cylindrical body that tapers at either end. The head is pointed and the lower jaw is prominent. The two dorsal fins are separated and on a level with the ventral and anal fins. The caudal fin is forked and has pointed margins. These barracuda are silvery, darker dorsally, with black fins. Maximum length two meters.

Habitat

It lives both near the reef and in the open sea. It frequents the surface more, and lives at a depth of up to 100 meters.

Distribution

This species is quite widespread in all tropical and subtropical seas.

Biology and Behavior

A formidable hunter, as can be seen in its strong teeth, this species feeds on fish, crustaceans and cephalopods. Although the adults are solitary, the juveniles form schools in lagoons or near the outer reef.

Great Barracuda

79

Sphyraena barracuda

min ▬▬▬▬▬▬▬▬▬▬ max
index of dangerousness

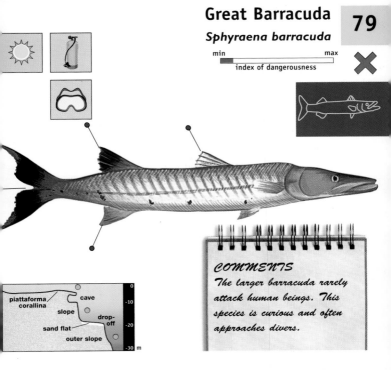

piattaforma corallina
cave
slope
drop-off
sand flat
outer slope

0
-10
-20
-30 m

COMMENTS
The larger barracuda rarely attack human beings. This species is curious and often approaches divers.

Ecsenius gravieri

BLENNIES – GOBIES

The **Blennidae** family lives in all seas and in the Indo-Pacific region is represented by more than 100 species, all of them less than 15 centimeters long. Blennies have a long scaleless body covered with a thin layer of protective mucus, and a single, long dorsal fin that often stretches from the head to the caudal apex. In some genera the head is square, with small tentacles under the eyes, while in other genera the head is oval and the mouth has pointed teeth. Blennies are territorial and like to stay in small holes in the reef or in rubble; depending on the genus, they are either carnivorous or herbivorous. During the evolutionary process some species lost their air bladder. **Gobies** are also small fishes. They belong to the Gobiidae family and, like the blennies, are small, with a large mouth with conical teeth, small scales on their body, and continuous and not divided ventral fins. This family has the most species in the world—over 1,500—a third of which live in the Indo-Pacific region. In general, gobies live on soft corals or sponges, are territorial and sedentary, and are carnivorous, even though certain genera feed on zooplankton. Some live in symbiosis with small shrimp, with which they live together in the same lair.

Common genera in the Red Sea: Blennidae - *Ecsenius, Plagio-tremus, Cirripectes*; Gobidae - *Bryaninops, Valenciennea, Gobiodon*.

Midas Blenny

Ecsenius midas (Starck, 1969)

I **Blennide Mida**
D **Neonaugen-Wipp-Schwimmer**
F **Blennie Midas**

 13 cm

 2-30 m

PERCIFORMES

Blennidae

Description

A blenny with a long body and square head profile. The caudal fin is crescent-shaped with elongate margins. Its body has no scales but is mucosal. Its color varies from yellow to orange, but some individuals have a bluish coloration. Maximum length 13 cm.

Closely related species: *E. gravieri* and *E. frontalis*.

Habitat

It lives in environments with abundant coral growth along the outer reef slopes, at a depth of 2-30 meters.

Distribution

Quite widespread in the Red Sea, the Gulf of Aqaba and along the East African coast as far as the Marquesas Islands.

Biology and Behavior

It feeds on zooplankton, which it often catches by mingling with schools of anthias, whose swimming technique it imitates.

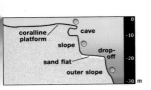

COMMENTS

Curious by nature, this blenny often hides in small holes, from which it emerges to observe the surroundings.

Maiden Goby

Valenciennea puellaris (Tomiyama, 1956)

I **Ghiozzo donzella**
D **Maiden-Schläfergrundel**
F **Gobie dormeur à taches orange**

 17 cm

2-30 m

PERCIFORMES

Gobiidae

Description
A goby that is flat ventrally, with a posteriorly compressed body and rounded tail. The high-set eyes are protuberant. The separate ventral fins are used to lift the body up from the substrate. It is whitish, with orange vertical stripes and spots on its sides.
Maximum length 17 cm.

Habitat
It lives on sandy bottoms in lagoons or on the seaward side of the reef at a depth of 2-30 meters.

Distribution
Indo-Pacific region, from the Red Sea to Japan and the Great Barrier Reef in Australia.

Biology and Behavior
It lives in couples in holes that it digs in the sandy bottom with its mouth. These lairs are often under rocks or rubble. It moves around by using its pectoral fins for propulsion.

Maiden Goby

81

Valenciennea puellaris

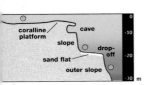

COMMENTS

More common in the northern Red Sea. A very popular species in tropical sea aquariums, therefore important commercially.

Acanthurus sohal (#83)

SURGEONFISHES
UNICORNFISHES
RABBITFISHES

Surgeonfishes and unicornfishes belong to the **Acanthuridae** family characterized by spines or extremely sharp bony blades at the sides of the caudal peduncle that are often highlighted by their bright color; these can inflict deep wounds. These fishes also have an ovoid body covered with small scales, a single dorsal fin and a tiny mouth in a terminal position. They are herbivorous or sometimes eat plankton. They are active by day and are not aggressive toward human beings, frequenting the reef platform, where they stay 30-80 centimeters under the surface, almost always in schools, but they also move to deep water along the reef slope. Surgeonfishes have a pair of retractile caudal spines that can be pushed forward if need be. Unicornfishes are recognizable for the long protuberance on the anterior part of the head (which is lacking in some species) and have two pairs of very sharp bony plates that are not retractile. Rabbitfishes (**Siganidae** family), related to the Acanthuridae, have a compressed body and poisonous spines on their continuous dorsal fin and on the ventral fins with which they inflict painful stings.

Common genera in the Red Sea:
Acanthurus, Zebrasoma, Naso, Siganus.

Black Surgeonfish

Acanthurus gahhm (Forsskål, 1775)

I **Pesce chirurgo nero**
D **Schwarzer Doktorfisch**
F **Chirurgien noir à larme noire**

 40 cm

 1-40 m

Description

An oval, compressed body with elongate margins on the caudal fin, which is crescent-shaped. Its mouth is slightly protruding. This surgeonfish is black, with a vertical white band at the base of its tail. It has two retractile spines on the caudal peduncle. Maximum length 40 cm. Related species: *A. nigricauda*, for which it is easily mistaken.

Habitat

It lives along the entire edge of the reef at a depth of up to 40 meters.

Distribution

An endemic Red Sea and Gulf of Aden species whose presence in other areas of the Indo-Pacific region is controversial.

Biology and Behavior

It feeds on rubble, algae and various invertebrates, even planktonic ones. If often moves in schools near coralline formations. It is curious and often approaches and even follows divers.

Black Surgeonfish

Acanthurus gahhm

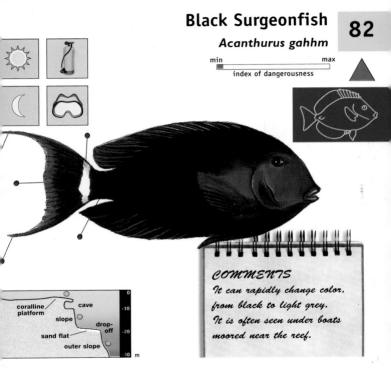

82

min   max
index of dangerousness

COMMENTS

It can rapidly change color,
from black to light grey.
It is often seen under boats
moored near the reef.

coralline platform
cave
slope
drop-off
sand flat
outer slope

E

Acanthuridae

Sohal Surgeonfish

Acanthurus sohal (Forsskål, 1775)

I **Pesce chirurgo sohal**
D **Sohal-Doktorfisch**
F **Chirurgien d'Arabie**

40 cm

0-10 m

Description

An oval, compressed body with a strongly crescent-shaped tail. Typical coloration, with grey and blue horizontal stripes that become darker on the top and sides. The fins are black with blue borders, except for the pectoral fin, which has a yellow spot. An orange spot is behind the operculum. The two retractile blades near the tail are orange. Maximum length 40 cm.

Habitat

It lives on the upper and outer edge of the reef, often in the undertow zone, at a depth of up to 10 meters.

Distribution

An endemic species of the Red Sea and the Arabian coasts, it has also been seen on the East African coast.

Biology and Behavior

A territorial species that is often aggressive with intruders. It feeds mainly on algae.

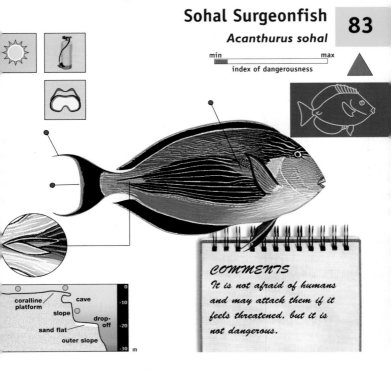

Sohal Surgeonfish

Acanthurus sohal

min max
index of dangerousness

COMMENTS

It is not afraid of humans and may attack them if it feels threatened, but it is not dangerous.

coralline platform

cave

slope

drop-off

sand flat

outer slope

0
-10
-20
-30 m

Sailfin Surgeonfish

Zebrasoma desjardinii (Bennett, 1836)

I **Pesce chirurgo dalle pinne a vela**
D **Brauner Segelflossendoktor**
F **Chirurgien voilier**

40 cm

1-30 m

PERCIFORMES

Acanthuridae

Description

A typical body shape with tall dorsal and anal fins. The mouth is ver
protuberant. This surgeonfish is brown, with vertical stripes of di
ferent colors. On the fins these stripes tend to become horizonta
The underbody and head are white-dotted. It has a pair of rectrac
tile blades on its caudal peduncle. Maximum length 40 cm.

Habitat

It lives in lagoon areas or on the outer edge of the reef, at a dept
of up to 30 meters.

Distribution

Common in the Red Sea and the entire Indo-Pacific region.

Biology and Behavior

It feeds on algae, which it gathers among the corals. During the da
it lives in couples, but it may form large schools in the late afternoor
The juveniles, lighter in color, take shelter among the acropor
branches.

Sailfin Surgeonfish

Zebrasoma desjardinii

min ▬▬▬ max
index of dangerousness

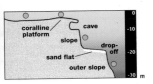

coralline platform
cave
slope
drop-off
sand flat
outer slope

0
-10
-20
-30 m

COMMENTS

A very territorial species that sometimes moves in schools of 50-100. It may be mistaken for a related species, Z. veliferum.

Blue Sailfin Tang

Zebrasoma xanthurum (Blyth, 1852)

I **Pesce chirurgo dalla coda gialla**
D **Blauer Segelflossendoktor**
F **Chirurgien queue jaune**

22 cm

0-20 m

Description

The tall, compressed body is distinguished by its wide dorsal fin and sharply tapered mouth. The body is electric blue, with darker spots on the head and underbody. The tail is yellow, like the margin of the pectoral fins. A retractile blade is on each side of the caudal peduncle. Maximum length 22 cm.

Habitat

It lives on the outer slope of the reef at a depth of up to 20 meters.

Distribution

Mainly in the Red Sea and Persian Gulf, but it has also been seen in the Maldives Islands.

Biology and Behavior

This fish often lives in schools and feeds mainly on stringy algae, which it manages to grab even in the smallest crevices thanks to its long, thin mouth.

Blue Sailfin Tang

Zebrasoma xanthurum

min   max
index of dangerousness

COMMENTS

A very popular species in aquariums. At night it takes on lighter colors.

coralline platform
cave
slope
drop-off
sand flat
outer slope

0
-10
-20
-30 m

Sleek Unicornfish

Naso hexacanthus (Bleeker, 1855)

I **Pesce unicorno liscio**
D **Blauklingen-Nasendoktor**
F **Nason gris**

75 cm

6-137 m

PERCIFORMES

Acanthuridae

Description
A spindle-shaped body with a truncate tail and regularly shaped head without a rostrum. The coloration varies from olive green to grey, lighter on the underbody. Those more than 25 cm long have black tongues. Two blades are on either side of the caudal peduncle. Maximum length 75 cm.

Habitat
It likes the outer reef slope and the open sea.

Distribution
Red Sea and entire Indo-Pacific region.

Biology and Behavior
A diurnal species that lives in large schools in the exposed parts of the reef and in the open sea, where it feeds on zooplankton. It occasionally eats algae, too. The coloration may change according to the mood of the fish. At night it rests on the reef.

Sleek Unicornfish

Naso hexacanthus

min max

index of dangerousness

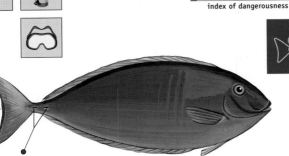

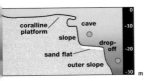

COMMENTS
During courtship the males'
head and the anterior portion
of the body become blue.

Orangespine Unicornfish

Naso lituratus (Forster, 1801)

I **Pesce unicorno arancione**
D **Gelbklingen-Doktorfisch**
F **Nason à éperons orange**

45 cm

0-90 m

PERCIFORMES

Description

An oval, elongate body, with a prominent mouth. The caudal fin has two long filaments at the ends. The body is dark grey, the dorsal fin is black at the base and yellow on the margin. A black band with a yellow border covers the eyes and mouth. The four non-retractile blades on the caudal peduncle are orange and quite conspicuous. Maximum length 45 cm.

Habitat

It can be seen in lagoons or on the seaward slope of the reef, from the surface to 90 meters' depth. It prefers areas rich in algae.

Distribution

The entire Indo-Pacific region.

Biology and Behavior

A basically herbivorous species, it feeds mostly on brown algae. It lives singly or in couples, but may also form large schools or mingle with other species while looking for food.

Acanthuridae

Orangespine Unicornfish

Naso lituratus

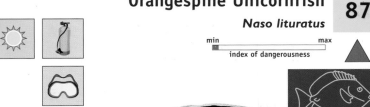

min ———————————————— max
index of dangerousness

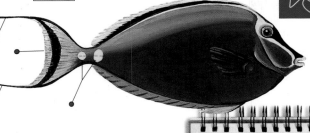

coralline platform
cave
slope
drop-off
sand flat
outer slope

0
-10
-20
-30 m

COMMENTS

This species lacks the typical frontal protuberance after which unicornfishes were named. Common in the Hurghada region.

Bluespine Unicornfish

Naso unicornis (Forsskål, 1775)

I **Pesce unicorno blu**
D **Kurznasendoktorfisch**
F **Nason à éperons bleus**

70 cm

1-80 m

PERCIFORMES

Description

The body is oval, taller in the anterior portion and tapering toward the tail, which is truncate and has long terminal filaments. The profile has a robust frontal horn that is more developed in the males. This species is olive green-grey and the four blades on the caudal peduncle are blue. Maximum length 70 cm.

Habitat

This unicornfish lives in brackish canals, lagoons or on the outer reef from the surface to a depth of about 80 meters.

Distribution

The entire Indo-Pacific region, from the Red Sea to Japan and Hawaii

Biology and Behavior

Basically a herbivorous and diurnal species. It moves about in small schools in the fringe zones.

Acanthuridae

Bluespine Unicornfish

Naso unicornis

min ━━━━━━━━━━━━━━ max
index of dangerousness

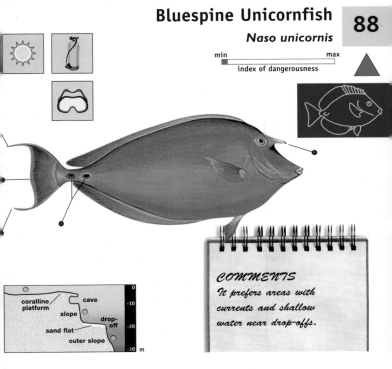

COMMENTS
It prefers areas with currents and shallow water near drop-offs.

coralline platform
cave
slope
drop-off
sand flat
outer slope

0
-10
-20
-30 m

Stellate Rabbitfish

Siganus stellatus (Forsskål, 1775)

I   **Pesce coniglio stellato**
D   **Tüpfel-Kaninchenfisch**
F   **Poisson-lapin étoilé**

 40 cm

 1-27 m

PERCIFORMES

Siganidae

Description

An oval body with a slightly elongate mouth and forked tail. The dorsal, anal and ventral fins are supported by erectile and poisonous spinous rays. The terminal lobes of these fins are broad, extending toward the caudal peduncle. Coloration grey or olive green, with a great many black dots. The unpaired fins have yellow borders, and the forehead is also yellow. Related species: *S. puelloides*.

Habitat

It lives in lagoons or on the outer reef.

Distribution

Widespread in the Red Sea and from the East African coast to the Andaman Islands.

Biology and Behavior

A diurnal species that rests on the bottom, changing its coloration. It feeds on algae and zooplankton. The juveniles tend to be gregarious, while the adults live in couples.

Siganus stellatus

min ▬▬▬▬▬▬▬ max
index of dangerousness

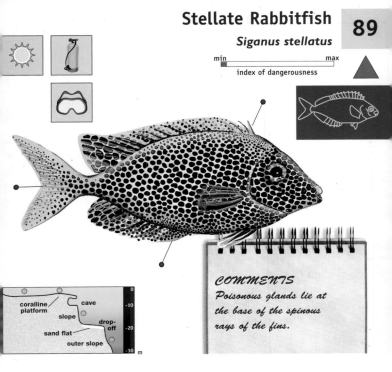

COMMENTS
Poisonous glands lie at the base of the spinous rays of the fins.

coralline platform
cave
slope
drop-off
sand flat
outer slope

0
-10
-20
-30 m

Caranx sexfasciatus (#92)

TREVALLIES

There are over 200 species of trevallies in the temperate and tropical zones; these typical predators belong to the **Carangidae** family, represented in the Red Sea by 47 species. Their size is medium or large (sometimes over 170 cm in length), and they are silvery with a yellow, bluish or green sheen, depending on the species. Their body is compressed laterally and convex dorsally, with tiny dorsal and ventral fins and well-developed, arched and thin pectoral fins. The caudal peduncle is narrow and the caudal fin is strongly forked and powerful. When Carangids swim quickly the first dorsal fin is retracted into a slit.

Trevallies live in schools, usually in open water, and go near the outer reef, particularly in areas with strong currents, in search of prey. They are excellent swimmers, able to go 50 km per hour, but must move about continuously to keep their balance, since their air bladder is virtually absent. These fishes are diurnal and feed on fish; they rarely live singly, but move about in large schools that may have hundreds of members and can easily be seen around the Ras Mohammed reefs. Trevallies are also important commercially, since they are much in demand as food.

Common genera in the Red Sea:
Caranx, Carangoides, Seriola, Trachinotus, Scomberoides.

253

Bluefin Trevally

Caranx melampygus (Cuvier, 1833)

I **Carango a pinne blu**
D **Blauflossenmakrele**
F **Carangue à nageoires bleues**

 100 cm

 1-190 m

PERCIFORMES

Carangidae

Description

A compressed body with a square frontal profile and a strongly forked crescent-shaped tail supported by a thin caudal peduncle. This species is silvery, tending to green dorsally and with small dark spots. The pectoral fins are yellowish, while the others are blue. Maximum length one meter, weight 44 kilograms.

Habitat

This trevally lives on the outer reef slope up to a depth of 190 meters. It sometimes frequents caves and rubble in search of glassfishes.

Distribution

Widespread in the entire Indo-Pacific region, from the Red Sea to the West Coast of the United States.

Biology and Behavior

It lives in very large schools that may frequent the inner bottoms of reefs. It follows larger fish in order to surprise its prey, consisting of fish and various invertebrates.

Bluefin Trevally

Caranx melampygus

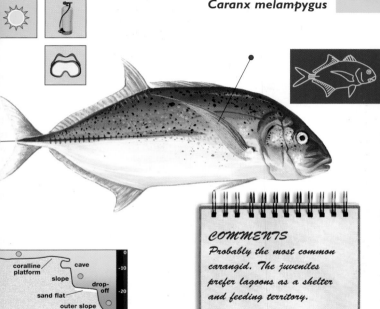

COMMENTS

Probably the most common carangid. The juveniles prefer lagoons as a shelter and feeding territory.

coralline platform
cave
slope
drop-off
sand flat
outer slope

0
-10
-20
-30 m

Giant Trevally

Caranx ignobilis (Forsskål, 1775)

- I **Trevally gigante**
- D **Dickkopfmakrele**
- F **Carangue géante**

 170 cm

 10-100 m

PERCIFORMES

Carangidae

Description

A large carangid that may be more than 1.7 meters long. It has a powerful, compressed body with an almost vertical frontal profile. The second dorsal fin and anal fin are very tall, the pectoral fins are long and the tail is forked. This species is grey dorsally, silver ventrally and with small black spots on the sides; the fins are grey.

Habitat

It lives in lagoons or, more frequently, in open water on the seaward reef slope, at a depth of 10-100 meters.

Distribution

Red Sea and Indo-Pacific region.

Biology and Behavior

A solitary, noctural species that spawns in shallow lagoon water or near shoals in the open sea. The juveniles congregate in lagoons and mangrove swamps. It feeds on fish, crustaceans and cephalopods.

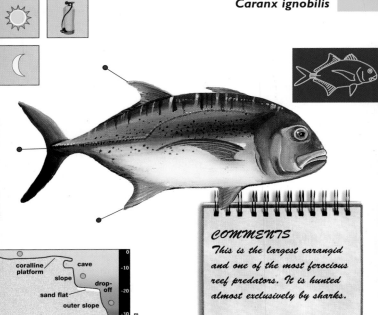

COMMENTS

This is the largest carangid and one of the most ferocious reef predators. It is hunted almost exclusively by sharks.

coralline platform · cave · slope · drop-off · sand flat · outer slope

Bigeye Jackfish

Caranx sexfasciatus (Quoy & Gaimard, 1825)

I   **Trevally occhio grosso**
D   **Großaugenmakrele**
F   **Carangue gros yeux**

85 cm

0-96 m

PERCIFORMES

Description

An oval body with a convex head profile and large eyes. A row of
bony plates lies on the posterior half of the sides as far as the tail.
The caudal fin is tall and forked. This species is blue or silvery green,
lighter ventrally. There is a black spot on the upper margin of the
operculum. Maximum length 85 cm.

Habitat

It likes open water on the outer reef up to a depth of 96 meters.

Distribution

Indo-Pacific region, from the Red Sea to the American coast.

Biology and Behavior

During the day it forms dense schools that tend to break up at
sunset. Very active at night, it hunts singly or in schools, making rapid
raids inside the reef. It feeds on fish and crustaceans.

Carangidae

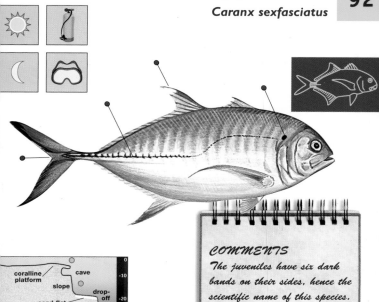

Bigeye Jackfish

Caranx sexfasciatus

COMMENTS

The juveniles have six dark bands on their sides, hence the scientific name of this species.

coralline platform

cave

slope

drop-off

sand flat

outer slope

0

-10

-20

-30 m

Goldbody (Orange-Spotted) Trevally

Carangoides bajad (Forsskål, 1775)

I **Carango arancione**
D **Orangenfleckmakrele**
F **Carangue dorée (C. à points orange)**

55 cm

2-50 m

Description

An oval, compressed body tapering at the ends. The thin, powerful caudal peduncle supports the tall, crescent-shaped tail. The median fins are triangular, while the pectoral fins are long and thin. This species has bronze coloration, silvery on the sides and ventrally, with gold spots on the sides. Maximum length 55 cm.

Habitat

This trevally lives along the reef slope at a depth of up to 50 meters and sometimes on sandy sea bottoms.

Distribution

Red Sea and Indo-Pacific region.

Biology and Behavior

It feeds mainly on fish and sometimes crustaceans. It hunts singly hiding among the corals, but it may also hunt for its prey in schools. It often mingles with *C. fulvoguttasus*. The caudal fin is its sole means of propulsion.

Goldbody (Orange-Spotted) Trevally

Carangoides bâjad

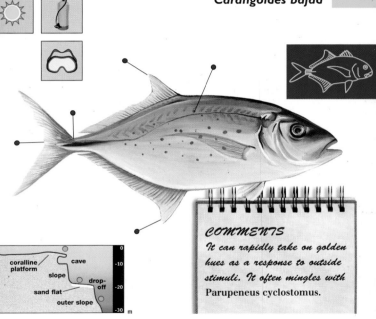

COMMENTS

It can rapidly take on golden hues as a response to outside stimuli. It often mingles with Parupeneus cyclostomus.

coralline platform

cave

slope

sand flat

drop-off

outer slope

0
-10
-20
-30 m

Balistoides viridescens (#95)

TRIGGERFISHES FILEFISHES

Triggerfishes are reef dwellers that belong to the **Balistidae** family. They vary in size (20-70 centimeters) and have oval, laterally compressed bodies covered with large, thick scales. The eyes are in an elevated position and the mouth has robust incisors able to crush madrepores. Their dorsal fin consists of three spines connected by a membrane that can be retracted and "locked" into a groove; this erectile mechanism allows these fishes to anchor themselves fast among the madrepores, a feature similar to that of the ancient ballista, hence their scientific name. The second dorsal fin and the anal fin are used for locomotion, while the caudal fin is used mostly as a rudder. The females lay their eggs in holes in the sand dug by the male, which then defends the nest. These are aggressive, territorial fishes and the larger species are dangerous for divers, especially during the reproduction period (July and August in the Red Sea). Filefishes (**Monacanthidae**), related to triggerfishes, have a flatter, longer body. The first dorsal fin consists virtually of only one thin ray and the skin is covered with smaller, sometimes rugose, scales that were once used as an abrasive.

Common genera in the Red Sea:
Balistapus, Balistoides, Pseudobalistes, Odonus, Rhinecanthus.

Orange-Striped Triggerfish

Balistapus undulatus (Park, 1797)

I   **Pesce balestra striato**
D   **Gelbschwanzdrücker**
F   **Baliste strié**

30 cm

2-50 m

Description

A rhomboid body that is longer than tall and compressed. The pro
file of the head is triangular. The first dorsal fin, supported by a
spinous ray, is taller than the second one. The tail is slightly rounded.
This species is brown or dark green, with diagonal orange stripes on
its sides and head. The caudal fin and the rays of the pectoral, dorsal
and anal fins are yellow-orange. Maximum length 30 cm.

Habitat

It likes sheltered areas abounding in corals, or reef slopes, at a depth
of up to 50 meters.

Distribution

Red Sea and Indo-Pacific region.

Biology and Behavior

A territorial but rather timid and only slightly aggressive species. Its
diet is varied: algae, fish and various invertebrates. It breaks madrepore
branches to eat their polyps.

Orange-Striped Triggerfish

Balistapus undulatus

min   max

index of dangerousness

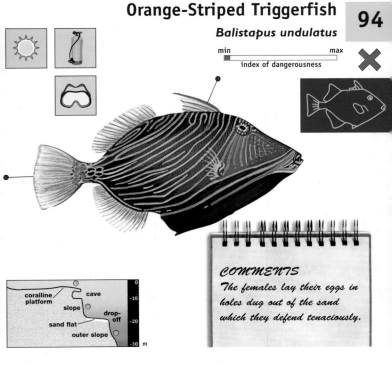

coralline platform

cave

slope

drop-off

sand flat

outer slope

0

-10

-20

-30 m

COMMENTS

The females lay their eggs in holes dug out of the sand which they defend tenaciously.

Giant Triggerfish

Balistoides viridescens (Bloch & Schneider, 1801)

I **Pesce balestra titano**
D **Riesendrücker**
F **Baliste à tête jaune**

75 cm

1-50 m

TETRAODONTIFORMES

Balistidae

Description
A massive oval body, and a large head with independent eyes. First dorsal fin erectile and with one spinous ray, second dorsal fin and anal fin tall anteriorly. Coloration yellowish, lighter on the caudal peduncle and around the mouth. The base and border of the fins are dark blue. A dark spot covers the eyes and operculum. Maximum length 75 cm.

Habitat
Sandy lagoons and the reef slope up to a depth of 50 meters.

Distribution
Red Sea and Indo-Pacific region.

Biology and Behavior
The juveniles are gregarious, while the adults are solitary and territorial, forming couples during the reproduction period. The females lay their eggs in the sand. The diet consists of sea urchins, starfish, corals and crustaceans, which it crushes with its powerful teeth.

Giant Triggerfish

Balistoides viridescens

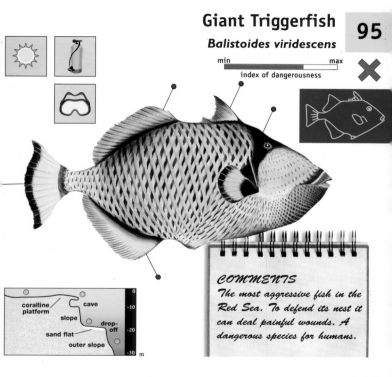

min   max
index of dangerousness

coralline platform
cave
slope
drop-off
sand flat
outer slope

0
-10
-20
-30
m

COMMENTS

The most aggressive fish in the Red Sea. To defend its nest it can deal painful wounds. A dangerous species for humans.

Blue Triggerfish

Pseudobalistes fuscus (Bloch & Schneider, 1801)

I **Pesce balestra blu**
D **Blauer Drücker**
F **Baliste à rides bleues**

55 cm

1-50 m

Description

A massive, oval body, the head occupying one-third of the body. The first dorsal fin is supported by a spinous ray; the second dorsal fin and the anal fin are tall, with a pointed anterior margin; caudal fin rounded, with elongate ends. The coloration is blue with yellow patterns that become more complex dorsally and on the head, while the fin margins are light blue.

Habitat

Sand flats at a depth of up to 50 m and sandy or detrital lagoons.

Distribuzione

Red Sea and Indo-Pacific region.

Biologia e comportamento

It feeds on crustaceans, mollusks, tunicates and sea urchins, which it upturns and attacks at the base. It lays eggs in a hole dug in the sand which it protects vigorously. The juveniles are gregarious, and are yellow with blue stripes.

Blue Triggerfish

Pseudobalistes fuscus

min   max
index of dangerousness

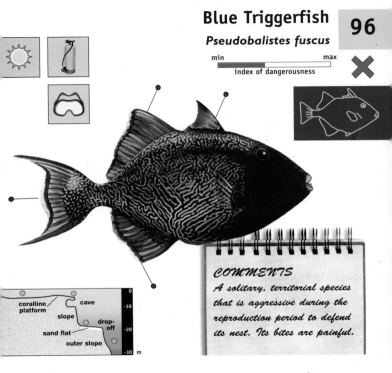

COMMENTS

A solitary, territorial species that is aggressive during the reproduction period to defend its nest. Its bites are painful.

coralline platform
cave
slope
drop-off
sand flat
outer slope

0
-10
-20
-30 m

Redtooth Triggerfish

Odonus niger (Rüppell, 1836)

I **Pesce balestra a denti rossi**
D **Rotzahndrücker**
F **Baliste bleu**

50 cm

5-40 m

TETRAODONTIFORMES

Balistidae

Description

An oval, compressed body that is rounded ventrally and with an inclined forehead. The lower jaw is prominent. The first dorsal fin has a spinous ray, the anal and second dorsal fins are very tall. A thin caudal peduncle and crescent-shaped tail with elongate margins. It is blue or violet, while the borders of the unpaired fins are lighter. Its teeth are red. Maximum length 50 cm.

Habitat

Often seen in schools in sand flats and sandy lagoons, or not far from reefs, at a depth of 5-40 meters.

Distribution

Red Sea and Indo-Pacific region.

Biology and Behavior

A gregarious, timid species that hides among the corals if threatened. When it does so, only the elongate margins of the caudal fin are visible. It feeds on zooplankton and sponges.

Redtooth Triggerfish

Odonus niger

min   max
index of dangerousness

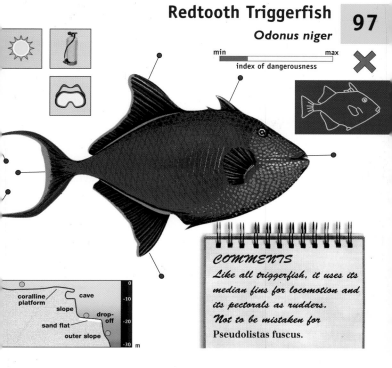

COMMENTS

Like all triggerfish, it uses its
median fins for locomotion and
its pectorals as rudders.
Not to be mistaken for
Pseudolistas fuscus.

coralline
platform   cave

slope

drop-off

sand flat

outer slope

0
-10
-20
-30 m

E

TETRAODONTIFORMES

Balistidae

Arabian Picassofish

Rhinecanthus assasi (Forsskål, 1775)

I **Pesce balestra Picasso**
D **Rotmeerpicassodrücker**
F **Baliste Picasso arabe**

30 cm

1-15 m

Description

Triangular head, posterior portion of the body oval, the first dorsal fin small and supported by a spinous ray. The caudal fin is truncate rounded in the middle. It is olive green dorsally, whitish ventrally; a black stripe with blue borders covers the eyes and operculum. Three black stripes are on the caudal peduncle and another one goes from base of the pectoral fins to the mouth, while an orange spot mark the anus. Maximum length 30 cm.

Habitat

It lives singly or in couples on sandy bottoms or along the reef slope from the surface to a depth of 15 meters.

Distribution

Red Sea and Persian Gulf.

Biology and Behavior

It feeds on sea urchins, crustaceans and other invertebrates.
The juveniles are gregarious and the adults basically solitary.

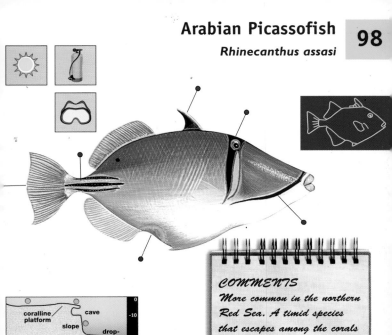

Arabian Picassofish

Rhinecanthus assasi

COMMENTS
More common in the northern
Red Sea. A timid species
that escapes among the corals
if disturbed.

coralline platform
cave
slope
sand flat
drop-off
outer slope
0
-10
-20
-30 m

Scribbled Filefish

Aluterus scriptus (Osbeck, 1765)

I **Pesce lima**
D **Besenschwanz-Feilenfisch**
F **Bourse écriture**

110 cm

2-80 m

TETRAODONTIFORMES

Monacanthidae

Description

An elongate, extremely compressed body tapering anteriorly and posteriorly, and a small upward-facing mouth. The long, rounded tail is often kept closed like a fan. Body olive-greenish, with black spots underscored by blue stripes. Maximum length over one meter.

Habitat

It lives in lagoons or on outer reef slopes at a depth of up to 80 meters.

Distribution

Widespread in all tropical and subtropical seas.

Biology and Behavior

A solitary species rarely seen in small schools, more often in couples. It is remarkably camouflaged when resting on madrepores. It feeds on algae, hydroids, medusas, gorgonians, anemones and tunicates. For locomotion it mainly uses its median fins.

Scribbled Filefish

Aluterus scriptus

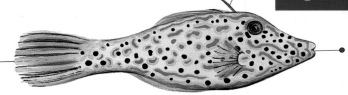

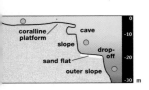

COMMENTS

A rather rare species.
The juveniles are pelagic,
gregarious and also take
shelter under floating objects.

Diodon hystrix (#102)

BOXFISHES
PUFFERFISHES
PORCUPINEFISHES

Boxfishes, pufferfishes and porcupinefishes all belong to the **Tetraodontiformes** order, the Greek name of which means that they have four teeth, or better, their teeth are fused in four plates. Lacking ventral fins, these fishes have a single dorsal fin above the anal fin. Propulsion is afforded by the pectoral fins and the anal fin, while the caudal fin serves as a rudder or to accelerate. Boxfishes (**Ostraciidae** family) have a quadrangular body covered with hexagonal bony plates that are like armor and are in turn covered with a toxic mucus. They are flat ventrally.

Pufferfishes (**Tetraodontidae** family) owe their name to the fact that in case of danger they swell up, doubling their size, thanks to the dilatation of their gastric sac temporarily filled with water, which frightens their enemies, just as porcupinefishes (**Diodontidae** family) raise the spines on their scales for the same reason. If brought to the surface, pufferfishes can also swell up by swallowing air. All Tetraodontids are poisonous if swallowed, as their internal organs contain a lethal poison.

Common genera in the Red Sea:
Ostracion, Canthigaster, Arothron, Diodon, Chylomicterus.

Cube Boxfish

Ostracion cubicus (Linnaeus, 1758)

I **Pesce scatola giallo**
D **Gelber Kofferfisch**
F **Coffre jaune**

45 cm

1-45 m

Description

The quadrangular shape of the body is due to the presence of bony subcutaneous plates. The mouth faces downward and is surmounted by a protuberance. The margin of the fins is rounded. The females are yellowish, with white spots bordered in black, while the males are greyish, with black spots.

Habitat

It lives in lagoons or in sheltered areas on the seaward reef slope at a depth of up to 45 meters.

Distribution

Indo-Pacific region. The Red Sea population may be a separate species.

Biology and Behavior

A timid creature ready to hide among the corals if threatened. It forms small harems and feeds on algae and invertebrates. The juveniles are yellow, with large white spots, which in the Red Sea are bordered in black.

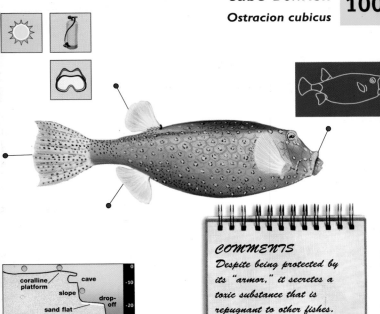

COMMENTS

Despite being protected by its "armor," it secretes a toxic substance that is repugnant to other fishes.

coralline platform
cave
slope
drop-off
sand flat
outer slope

0
-10
-20
-30 m

Masked Pufferfish

Arothron diadematus (Rüppell, 1829)

I **Pesce palla mascherato**
D **Maskenkugelfisch**
F **Tétrodon (Poisson globe) masqué**

30 cm

0-20 m

Description
An oval, roundish body, with a short head and prominent mouth. The dorsal and ventral fins are rounded and black, while the caudal fin is straight and truncate. This species is olive green-grey, with a black mask over its eyes and pectoral fins. The mouth is bordered in black. Maximum length 30 cm.

Habitat
Common on coralline bottoms, even exposed ones, from the surface to a depth of 20 meters.

Distribution
It lives only in the Red Sea.

Biology and Behavior
Normally a solitary fish, but during the reproduction period it congregates in large schools, with several males for every female. It feeds on various invertebrates, but prefers the coral polyps of ramous madrepores.

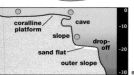

coralline platform
cave
0
-10
slope
drop-off
sand flat
-20
outer slope
-30 m

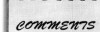

COMMENTS

Like all pufferfishes, it is able to swell up rapidly if it feels endangered.

Common Porcupinefish

Diodon hystrix Linnaeus, 1758

I **Pesce istrice**
D **Gewöhnlicher Igelfisch**
F **Grand porc-épic**

91 cm

2-50 m

Description

An elongate body weakly compressed dorsally. The head is short, with large eyes. The pectoral fins are well developed, the caudal rounded. It is covered with spines that stand upright when the body swells. Coloration greyish, darker dorsally, with small dark dots.

Habitat

It lives in lagoons and the outer reef up to a depth of 50 meters.

Distribution

Quite widespread in all tropical and subtropical seas.

Biology and Behavior

A solitary, nocturnal species that hides in reef crevices during the day. It feeds on sea urchins, mollusks and crustaceans, which it crushes with its fused, jaw-like teeth. The juveniles are pelagic. If threatened, it swells up to frighten its enemy.

Common Porcupinefish

Diodon hystrix

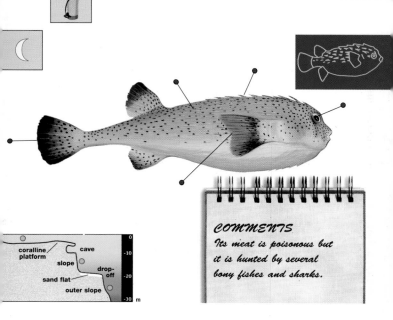

COMMENTS
Its meat is poisonous but it is hunted by several bony fishes and sharks.

coralline platform
cave
slope
drop-off
sand flat
outer slope

0
-10
-20
-30 m

BIBLIOGRAPHY

AA. VV., *Sharks & Rays*, London, 1997.

Debelius, H., *Indian Ocean Reef Guide*, Frankfurt, 1999.

Debelius, H., *Red Sea Reef Guide*, Frankfurt, 1998.

Edwards, J.A., Head, M.S., *Key Environments Red Sea*, London, 1985.

Froese, R., Pauly, D., *FishBase 2000: Concept, Design and Data Sources*, Philippines, 2000.

Harrison, P., Misiewicz, A., *Reef Fishes and Corals of the Red Sea*, London, 2000.

Hennemann, R.M., *Sharks and Rays*, Frankfurt, 2001.

Mojetta, A., Ghisotti, A., *Pesci e coralli del Mar Rosso*, Milano, 1996.

Mojetta, A., *Mar Rosso Paradiso Sommerso*, Vercelli, 1995.

Randall, J.E., *Sharks of Arabia*, London, 1986.

Randall, J.E., *Red Sea Reef Fishes*, London, 1983.

Sheppard, C., Price, A., Roberts, C., *Marine Ecology of the Arabian Region*, London, 1992.

Siliotti, A., *Sharm el-Sheikh Diving Guide*, Cairo, 1999.

Stafford-Deitsch, J., *Red Sea Sharks*, London, 1999.

Vine, P., *Red Sea Safety*, London, 1986.

http://www.fishbase.org

INDEX OF SCIENTIFIC NAMES

The numbers in **bold** type refer to the profile, those in Roman type refer to the page number.

Abudefduf sexfasciatus **69** 200
Abudefduf vaigiensis **68** 198
Acanthopagrus bifasciatus **35** 112
Acanthurus gahhm **82** 236
Acanthurus sohal **83** 238
Aethaloperca rogaa **25** 88
Aetobatus narinari **9** 38
Aluterus scriptus **99** 274
Amblyglyphidodon leucogaster **62** 186
Amphiprion bicinctus **67** 196
Antennarius coccineus **15** 60
Anthias taeniatus **31** 100
Apogon exostigma **33** 106
Arothron diadematus **101** 280
Balistapus undulatus **94** 264
Balistoides viridescens **95** 266
Bodianus axillaris **71** 206
Caesio lunaris **40** 128
Caesio suevica **41** 130

Carangoides bajad **93** 260
Caranx ignobilis **91** 256
Caranx melampygus **90** 254
Caranx sexfasciatus **92** 258
Carcharhinus albimarginatus **3** 24
Carcharhinus amblyrhynchos **2** 22
Carcharhinus melanopterus **4** 26
Cephalopholis miniata **24** 86
Cetoscarus bicolor **78** 222
Chaetodon auriga **52** 162
Chaetodon fasciatus **53** 164
Chaetodon larvatus **54** 166
Chaetodon lineolatus **55** 168
Chaetodon paucifasciatus **56** 170
Chaetodon semilarvatus **57** 172
Cheilinus undulatus **72** 208
Chromis dimidiata **65** 192
Chromis viridis **66** 194
Dascyllus aruanus **63** 188
Dascyllus trimaculatus **64** 190
Diodon hystrix **102** 282
Ecsenius midas **80** 230
Epinephelus fasciatus **26** 90
Epinephelus malabaricus **27** 92

Epinephelus tauvina **28** 94
Fistularia commersonii **18** 70
Gorgasia sillneri **13** 54
Gymnothorax javanicus **11** 50
Heniochus intermedius **58** 174
Labroides dimidiatus **70** 204
Lethrinus nebulosus **42** 134
Lutjanus bohar **37** 120
Lutjanus gibbus **38** 122
Lutjanus monostigma **39** 124
Manta birostris **8** 36
Monotaxis grandoculis **43** 136
Mulloidichthys vanicolensis **46** 146
Myripristis murdjan **16** 64
Naso hexacanthus **86** 244
Naso lituratus **87** 246
Naso unicornis **88** 248
Odonus niger **97** 270
Ostracion cubicus **100** 278
Oxycirrhites typus **59** 178
Papilloculiceps longiceps **23** 82
Paracirrhites forsteri **60** 180
Parapriacanthus guentheri **45** 142
Parupeneus cyclostomus **47** 148
Parupeneus forsskali **48** 150

Pempheris vanicolensis **44** 140
Platax orbicularis **36** 116
Plectorhinchus gaterinus
34 110
Pomacanthus imperator
50 156
Pomacanthus maculosus
49 154
Pomacentrus sulfureus **61** 184
Priacanthus hamrur **32** 104
Pseudanthias squamipinnis
30 98
Pseudobalistes fuscus **96** 268
Pterois miles **20** 76
Pygoplites diacanthus **51** 158
Rhincodon typus **6** 30
Rhinecanthus assasi **98** 272
Sargocentrum spiniferum
17 66
Scarus ferrugineus **75** 216
Scarus (Chlorurus) gibbus
76 218
Scarus (Chlorurus) sordidus
77 220
Scorpaenopsis diabolus **22** 80
Siderea grisea **12** 52
Siganus stellatus **89** 250
Sphyraena barracuda **79** 226
Sphyrna lewini **5** 28
Synanceia verrucosa **21** 78
Synodus variegatus **15** 58

Taeniura lymma **7** 34
Thalassoma rueppellii
73 210
Thalassoma lunare **74** 212
Torpedo panthera **10** 40
Triaenodon obesus **1** 20
Tylosurus choram **19** 72
Valenciennea puellaris **81** 232
Variola louti **29** 96
Zebrasoma desjardinii **84** 240
Zebrasoma xanthurum **85** 242

INDEX OF COMMON NAMES

The numbesr in **bold** type refer to the profile, those in Roman type refer to the page number.

Arabian angelfish **49** 154
Arabian grouper **28** 94
Arabian Picassofish **98** 272
Axilspot hogfish **71** 206
Banded dascyllus **63** 188
Batfish **36** 116
Bicolour parrotfish **78** 222
Bigeye emperor **43** 136

Bigeye jackfish **92** 258
Black surgeonfish **82** 236
Black-spotted grunt **34** 110
Blacktip grouper **26** 90
Blacktip reef shark **4** 26
Blue sailfin tang **85** 242
Blue triggerfish **96** 268
Bluefin trevally **90** 254
Bluegreen puller **66** 194
Bluespine unicornfish **88** 248
Blue-spotted stingray **7** 34
Bullethead parrotfish **77** 220
Cave sweeper (Hatchetfish)
44 140
Cleaner wrasse **70** 204
Common bigeye **32** 104
Common lizardfish **14** 58
Common porcupinefish
102 282
Coral grouper **24** 86
Cornetfish **18** 70
Crocodilefish **23** 82
Cube boxfish **100** 278
Devil scorpionfish **22** 80
Domino **64** 190
Doublebar bream **35** 112
Emperor angelfish **50** 156
Eyeshadow cardinalfish
33 106
Forsskål's goatfish **48** 150
Forster's hawkfish **60** 180

Freckled frogfish **15** 60
Giant moray **11** 50
Giant trevally **91** 256
Giant triggerfish **95** 266
Glassfish (Red Sea dwarf weeper) **45** 142
Goldbody trevally **93** 260
Great barracuda **79** 226
Grey moray **12** 52
Grey reef shark **2** 22
Half-and-half chromis **65** 192
Humpback snapper **38** 122
Klunzinger's wrasse **73** 210
Lined butterflyfish **55** 168
Lionfish **20** 76
Longnose hawkfish **59** 178
Lunar fusilier **40** 128
Maiden Goby **81** 232
Malabar grouper **27** 92
Manta ray **8** 36
Masked butterflyfish **57** 172
Masked pufferfish **101** 280
Midas blenny **80** 230
Moon grouper **29** 96
Moon wrasse **74** 212
Napoleonfish **72** 208
Onespot snapper **39** 124
Orangehead butterflyfish **54** 166
Orangespine unicornfish **87** 246

Orange-striped triggerfish **94** 264
Panther torpedo ray **10** 40
Red Sea anemonefish **67** 196
Red Sea bannerfish **58** 174
Red Sea fairy basslet **31** 100
Red Sea garden eel **13** 54
Red Sea needlefish **19** 72
Red Sea steep-headed parrotfish **76** 218
Redmouth grouper **25** 88
Redtooth triggerfish **97** 270
Royal angelfish **51** 158
Rusty parrotfish **75** 216
Sabre squirrelfish **17** 66
Sailfin surgeonfish **84** 240
Scalefin anthias **30** 98
Scalloped hammerhead shark **5** 28
Scissortail sergeant **69** 200
Scribbled filefish **99** 274
Sergeant major **68** 198
Silvertip shark **3** 24
Sleek unicornfish **86** 244
Sohal surgeonfish **83** 238
Spangled emperor **42** 134
Spotted eagle ray **9** 38
Stellate rabbitfish **89** 250
Stonefish **21** 78
Striped butterflyfish **53** 164
Suez fusilier **41** 130

Sulphur damselfish **61** 184
Threadfin butterflyfish **52** 162
Twinspot snapper **37** 120
Whale shark **6** 30
Whitebelly damselfish **62** 186
White-edged soldierfish **16** 64
Whitetip reef shark **1** 20
Yellowfin goatfish **46** 146
Yellowsaddle goatfish **47** 148

Pomacanthus imperator (#50)

Distributed in Egypt by OSIRIS OFFICE FOR BOOKS AND REVIEWS

50, Kasr el Nil Str CAIRO (Egypt) tel. & fax 02 - 39 11 489 e-mail: osiris@menanet.net